Becoming a Learner in the Workplace:
A Student's Guide to Practice-based and Work-based Learning in Health and Social Care

Becoming a Learner in the Workplace: A Student's Guide to Practice-based and Work-based Learning in Health and Social Care

By Mark Wareing

QUAY
BOOKS

A division of MA Healthcare Ltd

Quay Books Division, MA Healthcare Ltd, St Jude's Church, Dulwich Road, London SE24 0PB

British Library Cataloguing-in-Publication Data
A catalogue record is available for this book

© MA Healthcare Limited 2016

ISBN-13: 978 1 85642 508 7

Printed by Mimeo, Huntingdon, Cambridgeshire

WEST HERTS COLLEGE

CONTROL 92840

ITEM 4540776031

CLASS 362.107 WAR

DATE 27/04/16

£12.99

Contents

Preface   vi

Author biography   x

Chapter 1
Understanding practice-based and work-based learning   1

Chapter 2
Being at work and working for an organisation   17

Chapter 3
Using the Me, My, More, Must approach to learning   27

Chapter 4
Making sense of your role, practice and service users   41

Chapter 5
Being a worker and a learner   55

Chapter 6
Using your workplace for learning   75

Chapter 7
Becoming a health and social care professional   95

Chapter 8
**Practice-based and work-based learning:
ten key themes**   113

Appendices: 123
1: Blank dartboard   2: SWOT analysis template
3: PESTLE analysis template   4: Blank learning agreement

Preface

This student guide has been written to help support you to engage in practice-based and work-based learning in a range of health and social care settings. An increasing number of students are undertaking health and social care studies that involve placement learning, including those studying at higher apprenticeship and foundation degree level that are seeking to use clinical workplaces and practice areas for learning. This book has also been written for students studying traditional undergraduate health professions such as nursing and midwifery, and will be useful for those undertaking practice-based learning in radiography, social work, occupational and physiotherapy.

I have attempted to provide the reader with a thorough understanding of the challenges and opportunities of practice-based and work-based learning. Such learning requires a range of skills, strategies, techniques and attitudes that will empower readers to be fully equipped to engage in participatory workplace learning.

The main thread within the text is to differentiate between work-based and practice-based learning. This has been achieved by using a series of vignettes featuring two imaginary students: Sarbjit, a pre-registration nursing student studying for a BSc (Hons) in adult nursing; and Dave, a trainee assistant practitioner studying for a Foundation degree in health and social care. Although Sarbjit and Dave are imaginary characters, the vignettes have been written as 'fact–fiction' stories and drawn from my own experience as a nursing assistant, student and staff nurse, clinical nurse specialist, lecturer and educationalist.

A note on writing style and terminology

As this is a student guide, 'you' (the reader), has been adopted where it is necessary and appropriate to do so. I have written in the 'third' as opposed to the 'first' person when summarising particular topics and the key features of chapters. The terms 'patient', 'client' and 'service user' will be used to refer to those who receive care.

Activities

You will find a range of activities within each chapter that will require you to think about your own experience and the skills required to engage in practice- or work-based learning. It is entirely up to you as to when you complete each activity. You may find that completing each activity while reading the chapter is a useful way to 'break-up' your reading. Alternatively, you may wish to read the chapter straight through to allow yourself time to think and reflect before attempting an activity. Essentially, the purpose of the activities is to bring each chapter to life and enable you, as the reader, to engage with the text actively rather than passively.

Chapter-by-chapter overview

Chapter 1 discusses the importance of learning, and you will be introduced to Sarbjit in her first placement as a nursing student in order to make sense of the nature and purpose of practice-based learning. You will also be introduced to Dave, who is employed as a trainee assistant practitioner in an intermediate care team. You will see how he begins to acquire new knowledge while learning and working. Making sense of work and working within an organisation is explored in Chapter 2. In this chapter you will see that working within an organisation is inextricably linked to the development of your professional identity. In Chapter 3 you will be introduced to a new approach to reflection – the Me, My, More, Must model. This values-based model will require you to use your personal values and beliefs as the starting point for learning from experiences, situations and incidents that may have surprised or puzzled you. Chapter 4 contains some useful activities to help you make sense of your role, practice, patients and service users, and you will see how knowledge is gained by following Dave and Sarbjit as they participate in learning within their workplace and placement. Juggling the demands of being a worker and a learner is the focus of Chapter 5, which includes an exploration of communication, including how to hold a conversation that matters and how to negotiate. Both skills are critical when receiving and acting on feedback from mentors and seeking to secure learning opportunities. In Chapter 6, the practical challenges of and opportunities for using your workplace for learning is explored. We see in a vignette featuring Sarbjit how attending a ward meeting helped her to make sense of how a clinical team is led and how a decision is made through shared problem solving. This chapter also considers the importance of curiosity as a learning-to-learn strategy and provides you with guidance on how to prepare for placements, practice-based assessments, and how to manage your mentor. Chapter 7 is very practical, as the focus is on applying for and securing your first post as a qualified health and social care professional. We return to Sarbjit, who has now completed her nursing degree, to see how she secures her first staff nurse post. We explore what it means to be a professional and how authentic professional practice can be supported by being involved in coaching and mentoring. The final chapter identifies ten key themes from the book and explores how you can use skilled influence to become a change practitioner.

Acknowledgements

I would like to thank two of my former colleagues at Birmingham City University, Joy Hall and Dr Marion Thompson, for providing me with protected writing time and allowing me to use learning and teaching resources that I developed during my time in Edgbaston. Daniel Kirkham, who is currently studying adult nursing at Birmingham City University, gave me permission to use his beautifully crafted mind map in Chapter 4. My colleagues at the University of Bedfordshire have made me feel very welcome and I am indebted to Dr Barbara Burden, who has ensured that I have had sufficient time to complete this book while developing other areas of my research and scholarship.

While writing this book I have been reminded of a large number of people who have supported my own practice-based and work-based learning throughout an interesting and varied career that has spanned over 25 years. I wish to record my debt of gratitude to the late Jenny Haywood of North East Worcestershire College; successive mentors and nurse tutors at the Heartlands Hospital and Birmingham College of Nurse Education; the late Gareth Owens, Steve Candler, Helena Paolozzi, Mr DWG Budd and Mr Jeremy Crew at Horton and Churchill Hospitals; and past and present undergraduate, postgraduate and doctoral students, who have provided me with the deepest and richest of learning experiences.

Mark Wareing
Adderbury, Oxfordshire

Author biography

Dr Mark Wareing has taught students in the areas of adult and acute care, paramedic science, administration and informatics, mental health and learning disabilities, rehabilitation, end-of-life care, long-term conditions, childcare, radiography, radiotherapy, mammography, defence health and welfare settings. This experience has enabled him to develop an interest in work-based and practice-based learning and to publish research on mentoring and the lived experience of work-based learners in a number of national and international journals.

Mark completed his nurse training at the Birmingham College of Nurse Education and held a number of posts in medicine and surgery before establishing the specialist urological nursing service in North Oxfordshire as a clinical nurse specialist employed by the Department of Urology in Oxford. Before entering education, Mark served for 4 years as a captain in the Territorial Army Medical Services and undertook a 3-month operational tour in Iraq.

From 2004 to March 2015 Mark was an educational facilitator and then senior lecturer in health and social care at Birmingham City University. He is now Director of Practice Learning within the Department of Healthcare Practice at the University of Bedfordshire. Mark is a Fellow of the Higher Education Academy and holds academic associate membership of the Chartered Institute of Personnel and Development.

CHAPTER I

Understanding practice-based and work-based learning

By the end of this chapter you will be able to:

1. Discuss the importance of learning
2. Explain the difference between practice-based and work-based learning
3. Analyse how learning takes place within health and social care work-places.

Introduction

Why is it that the simplest of questions always seem to be the hardest to answer? This chapter will start by asking some quite simple questions that will allow you to make sense of practice-based and work-based learning as it occurs in health and social care settings. Hospitals, health centres, nursing and care homes have always been places where learning has taken place because they are places of work where students are sent on placements. This leads us to our first question: what do we mean by learning?

Learning

For centuries teachers have used a questioning approach to help learners to think and share their knowledge about a topic, which allows a teacher to iden-tify what a learner knows before moving to topics that are unknown to the learner. Bringing a topic to the attention of the learner is useful as it allows a learner to realise that they know more than he or she first thought, particularly if his or her knowledge has been gained from experience and has become 'hidden' (Eraut, 2004; Raelin, 2008). Sometimes the learner may reveal assumptions about a topic that teachers need to challenge, particularly if his or her assumptions influence how he or she values groups of people.

Activity 1

Think about the last time that you learnt something while working. Identify:
- Who helped you to learn and what they did and said
- What knowledge the experience brought to the surface (your hidden knowledge)
- Whether your assumptions were challenged as a result of the experience.

Learning is a very powerful force that not only shapes your knowledge and understanding of the world, but your behaviour. In fact, it could be argued that the greatest evidence that learning has taken place is when your behaviour changes.

It is also important to remember that you can have knowledge, but lack understanding. In other words you may be able to recall facts and figures from memory, but lack the ability to link your knowledge to make sense of a situation or solve a problem. In order to 'problem solve' you not only select a course of action, but must select the right course of action from a range of possible options. A 'course of action' might be the most appropriate way of encouraging a patient to try to dress him- or herself or how to communicate effectively in order to involve a client's spouse or partner in his or her rehabilitation. Once you have executed your chosen course of action you should be able to justify why you have acted in the way you have. If that course of action has been enacted for the first time, then change has occurred. If you are able to provide a sound explanation for your actions based on your knowledge, you have demonstrated your understanding.

It is important to differentiate between knowledge and information, not least as there are many sources of information available to you. Although information is readily available and accessible via the internet, you need to have knowledge and understanding in order to select information appropriately. Faced with the need to make sense of knowledge and understanding, you also need to 'learn how to learn', and this is particularly vital when working in health and social care workplaces that are busy, messy and complex and where there is constant change and uncertainty. The next section of this chapter will explain the nature of practice-based learning. Once again, we will start with some simple questions.

The nature of practice-based learning

So what is practice-based learning? Clinical areas where doctors, nurses, midwives and therapists practise have long been used for practice-based learning, both by those seeking to qualify and enter a profession and by healthcare professionals seeking to learn from their day-to-day practice. Traditionally within health and social care, students have used placements in a range of settings in order to learn to practise before qualification. Entrance to a profession is signified by a newly-qualified practitioner's name being placed on a register maintained by professional bodies such as the General Medical Council, Nursing and Midwifery Council or Health and Care Professions Council. It is the professional body that sets the requirements for registration through the accreditation of higher education institutions that are permitted to run pre-registration programmes such as nursing, midwifery, social work or radiography. One of those requirements will be a minimum amount of practice-based learning undertaken via placement in suitable clinical, therapeutic or practice environments. For example, nursing students must spend at least 50% of their time engaging in practice-based learning in order to complete their pre-registration programme. Practice-based learning is therefore associated with professional education or 'education by and for' a profession, where learning is controlled by a particular occupational group to ensure that what a trainee promises to do, they later fulfil as a member of their chosen profession (Nettleton, 2013).

It is important to point out that there is a difference between the words practice and practise; a little confusing as both words (like all 'homophones') are pronounced the same but have different meanings:

The word 'practice' means the carrying out, or the exercise of a profession; for example medicine, nursing or social work. This is a noun, a word used as the name of a person, place, or thing; or a 'describing' word.

The word 'practise' means to exercise the skills of one's trade or profession; or to exercise one's professional skill. This is a verb (a word indicating an action, state or occurrence) – a 'doing' word.

(Oxford Dictionary of English, 2005)

We could therefore describe a support worker reflecting on her practice in order to improve her practise. When you practice or perform something, you do so repeatedly. Through practise you seek to learn from your mistakes and become aware that your performance varies. This is a key feature of practice-based learning that occurs in response to different episodes of care work where your ideas and observations become linked towards the end of each placement (Price, 2012).

Practice-based learning is reliant on experience that occurs when you are 'placed' in particular situations to enable you to learn in and about practice through authentic experiences while becoming part of a community of practice formed from a particular professional group (Lave and Wenger, 1991). Some of the most effective and richest learning experiences occur, however, when you are on a placement where there is a mixture of different professionals and where learning becomes interprofessional as it occurs when you work between professional groups (Thistlethwaite, 2013). Learning from experience is also called 'experiential learning' and is an activity that includes 'learning by doing' as well as learning from life experiences, which is important as you need to relate what has been learnt to your current understanding by building on your existing knowledge.

Burnard (2002) reminds us that while every situation is a potential learning situation, we do not necessarily learn from everything we do and that we need to 'notice' not only what is happening but to 'notice ourselves'. This is achieved by using reflection, which is a tool to help you learn by noticing what is happening around you while looking within yourself to identify what you are thinking and feeling. This last point brings us back nicely to the start of this chapter. By noticing what you do and then reflecting on your reasons for doing it, and by identifying your thoughts and feelings, you can start to change your behaviour and in doing so know that learning has taken place. Let us consider an example of practice-based learning using our first vignette.

Vignette 1 demonstrates what we mean by practice-based learning. Sarbjit is a new nursing student on her first clinical placement, a urology ward where there are patients with urinary problems such as prostate, bladder and kidney disorders as a result of disease or cancer. Many of her patients will be elderly and some will have been admitted to the ward for surgery while others will be recovering from surgery. The ward is busy and admits patients from the accident and emergency department with painful conditions such as retention of urine, kidney stones or even bladder trauma. Many patients have indwelling urinary catheters and nearly all patients who have been to theatre have intravenous infusions (drips) and drains from surgical wounds. Although Sarbjit

Vignette 1: Sarbjit and her first clinical placement

Sarbjit is a first-year adult nursing student. Before enrolling on the BSc Adult Nursing degree programme, Sarbjit was an authorised volunteer in her local general hospital, which included helping out with fundraising activities and working on the hospital help desk for a few hours each weekend. She also worked as a healthcare assistant in a nursing home for a year before applying for university.

Sarbjit is 3 weeks into her first placement on a urology ward in a large inner city NHS hospital. Mandy, a staff nurse who has been qualified for 5 years, is Sarbjit's mentor. So far Sarbjit has worked six shifts with Mandy. Will is the practice placement manager and a senior charge nurse based on another acute surgical ward.

One afternoon Will drops into the ward to speak to the ward manager and sees Mandy on duty. He takes the opportunity to invite her to the next mentor update meeting and asks her how Sarbjit has settled into the ward. Mandy explains that Sarbjit has settled into the ward well; she makes notes during the patient handover meetings, has asked Mandy whether they can arrange meetings to discuss things, and has identified some personal learning objectives for her placement.

Mandy explains that 2 days ago she and Sarbjit were bed-bathing a patient who suddenly became short of breath and went into cardiac arrest. She says that although Sarbjit remained calm and composed and was present during the attempt to resuscitate the patient, she was very shaky and tearful afterwards and needed to talk about the experience, which she described as 'sudden, shocking and distressing'. Sarbjit had been advised by Mandy to write a reflection piece based on her experience of witnessing her first cardiac arrest and share it with Mandy at their next meeting.

Mandy asked Will whether the nursing students had received any teaching about cardiac arrest situations before starting their first clinical placements. Will was able to confirm that the university had provided training on basic life support, including what to do and what to expect during a cardiac arrest situation.

has some hospital experience and has worked in a nursing home, adjusting to her first ward has been a powerful and challenging experience and that is why Mandy has made sure that she has worked with Sarbjit as much as possible to ensure she is supported and made to feel part of the team. Will, the practice placement manager, is also aware that new nursing students need support to adjust to their first ward and that is why he asked Mandy how Sarbjit was getting along. Mandy has been impressed by Sarbjit's keenness to learn, in particular her request to arrange meetings with Mandy to discuss her learning objectives. Mandy was also impressed by Sarbjit's reaction to the cardiac arrest situation and is concerned that students are suitably prepared for the ward and the prospect of witnessing their first cardiac arrest. Although Sarbjit experienced death and dying before when she worked in the nursing home, her past experience had not fully prepared her for the cardiac arrest that she witnessed and that is why, quite naturally, she was shaken by the experience. Sarbjit may have felt embarrassed by her emotions following the cardiac arrest, as she may have assumed that she should be able to cope with the situation given her previous experience.

Kilgallon and Thompson (2012) comment that students respond to new experiences based on their assumptions, expectations, knowledge, attitudes and emotions, which they use to interpret each new experience. In order for Sarbjit to make sense of her experience, Mandy therefore encouraged Sarbjit to write a reflection piece to assist her in making sense of the situation that she was involved with by identifying her feelings and further learning needs. As Sarbjit had a sudden and shocking experience, it is important that Mandy and Will ensure that she is supported. As this is her first placement, not only is Sarbjit being introduced to a completely new workplace, but a completely new clinical and professional environment where she needs to feel sufficiently comfortable in order to learn from the many and varied experiences that the ward affords her.

The nature of work-based learning

In the last section we explored the importance of learning, the difference between knowledge, understanding and information and how students, like Sarbjit, are introduced to practice through the use of placements where 'learning by doing' occurs. But what is work-based learning? On the surface practice-based and work-based learning appear to be the same. There are, however, some key differences.

Work-based learning has been described as learning from work and learning in work (Boud and Solomon, 2001). This means that each aspect of your work needs to be viewed as a learning opportunity that requires you to use a wide range of people, places and resources. In work-based learning, learning is acquired in the midst of action and dedicated to the task at hand (Williams, 2010). A key approach to work-based learning is participation, which means that you must be given the opportunity to participate in work and be exposed to a daily 'menu' of activities that provide or 'afford' you with a learning experience (Billett, 2004).

Although the learner might be a newcomer, a novice or an apprentice, work-based learners are normally employed by the organisation where their learning takes place. This is different to practice-based learning as students always start each placement as a newcomer, regardless of whether they are at the start of their course of study and therefore a novice, or at the end and about to become a registered healthcare professional.

In practice-based learning you spend the first week or so of each placement adjusting to the new community of practice that exists within each ward, department, clinical or therapeutic team that you have been 'placed' into. When you undertake your early placements you should be enabled to participate in practice 'increasingly' as you develop your new skills, gain confidence and experience, and your competence is assessed (Rogoff, 1995; Cronin, 2014). In later placements you will be able to participate in practice once you have demonstrated your existing skills and competence to members of your team. In both instances you are being 'prepared for practice' and this process includes making a successful adjustment to each new community of practice, gaining confidence, learning new skills and becoming competent. It also involves you demonstrating and refining existing skills and competencies while preparing, eventually, for registration with a professional body as discussed at the start of this chapter.

Work-based learners are normally already part of the community of practice and participate in day-to-day practice by virtue of their status as employees of the organisation for whom they are employed. Work-based learners have an existing role as determined by their job description. Their employer may have decided to invest in the workforce, however, to enable employees to develop their knowledge, skills and roles to meet new service demands.

The greatest challenge for you as a work-based learner is adjusting to becoming a learner while being in employment and still fulfilling the role that

Vignette 2: Dave, a trainee assistant practitioner

Dave is a first-year foundation degree health and social care student and has been employed as a member of the intermediate care team for 7 years. Dave successfully completed his NVQ level 3 while working as a band 3 rehabilitation assistant. He applied to undertake the Foundation degree when his NHS city community trust decided to develop band 4 assistant practitioner roles. The intermediate care team comprises six physiotherapists, six occupational therapists, two community speech and language therapists and nine rehabilitation assistants, two of whom are trainee assistant practitioners.

Dave has arranged to undertake his first formative assessment with Kate, his workplace mentor, after a busy morning where Dave has visited five clients. Kate and Dave sit down in the staff room to undertake his practice-based assessment, which requires him to discuss the competencies contained within his assessment document.

Kate starts by asking Dave to explain what each competency means and how it might relate to his role, practice and patients. The first two sections of the competency document relate to confidentiality and health and safety. Dave demonstrates a good level of understanding of safe, effective and efficient practice in these areas and has a good knowledge of the trust confidentiality policy and the Health and Safety at Work etc Act 1974. The next set of competencies relates to the 'six Cs', which include care, compassion, competence, communication, courage and commitment. Although Dave is able to name each of the six Cs, his knowledge of the Trust policy on escalating concerns and whistle-blowing is quite weak. Kate asks Dave to talk about one of the patients he visited during the previous morning and asks him to suggest possible examples of care that might require him to escalate his concerns. Dave describes a range of possible scenarios and incidents that might arise in his day-to-day practise and then recalls an incident a while ago where he had to raise his concerns regarding the care that one of his service users had received.

At the end of the formative assessment Kate provides Dave with written feedback and suggests that he researches the concept of whistle-blowing and accesses the trust policy on escalating concerns via the intranet. Dave asks Kate whether they can get their diaries together to arrange a further formative assessment in 6 weeks' time, which is scheduled to occur a month before his final summative practice-based assessment is due in.

you were originally employed for. In Vignette 2 you will be introduced to Dave, a Foundation degree student who is undertaking work-based learning to make the transition to a new role.

Dave is an experienced rehabilitation assistant who has been employed by his city community trust in an intermediate care team for a number of years. He is fully immersed in his team and has experience of using his workplace for learning and personal development, having completed his NVQ 3 award. Although Dave works with a wide range of registered healthcare professionals including therapists, nurses, GPs and social workers, he has decided that he would rather undertake a Foundation degree and become a band 4 assistant practitioner instead of becoming a therapist as he enjoys his role and simply wants to 'do more' for his patients. Dave is thoroughly enjoying his course but has faced two challenges that have been quite different from his experience undertaking his NVQ award. The first has been making the transition to being a work-based learner, which has meant juggling study and attendance at university with his work. The second challenge has been the transition from being a rehabilitation assistant to becoming a trainee assistant practitioner. Dave experienced some conflict from his colleagues, who have questioned the need for him to attend university each week. He has learnt that becoming a work-based learning and assistant practitioner is a challenging experience, particularly when being employed in an organisation that is not used to the assistant practitioner role (Wareing, 2012).

You will have noticed that Dave has taken the lead in arranging his first and second formative assessments while being mindful of when his final summative assessment needs to be completed. This demonstrates that work-based learners need to be responsible for their own learning and have good negotiation skills. Kate, Dave's workplace mentor, has made sure that Dave understands what each of the competencies means and has steered Dave's learning to areas which should be familiar to him, including his role (who he is, what his employment means), his practice (what he does) and his patients (whom he cares for). Kate also uses the patients that Dave has visited before the assessment to enable Dave to make links between his 'personal knowledge' (Eraut, 2000) or what is known and familiar (his patients and the care that he has given that morning) to what is unknown (whistle-blowing and escalating concerns). While Kate is satisfied that Dave's practice is safe, effective and efficient, she has assessed that Dave lacks knowledge of the trust policy on escalating concerns and he is given feedback to read up on the concept of whistle-blowing and to familiarise himself with the standard operating procedure for escalating concerns within the trust. There are two reasons why this is important.

First, this is knowledge that Dave needs in order to become an assistant practitioner and meet the standard of work expected of a band 4 senior support worker. Second, without this knowledge Dave may fail his final summative assessment. The assessment will require him to demonstrate a good level of understanding of what actions to take when the care of patients falls below the standard that is appropriate, not only in general for all patients cared for by the City Community Trust but the standard that is specific to the intermediate care team where Dave hopes to become a fully qualified assistant practitioner.

Activity 2

Read Vignettes 1 and 2 again. Think about:
■ How you would feel and respond if you had the same experience as Sarbjit
■ What challenges Dave might face in being recognised as a learner compared to Sarbjit
■ How Sarbjit and Dave's mentors have used reflection and what the similarities and differences are between them

Table 1.1 Key characteristics of practice- and work-based learning

Practice-based learning:	Work-based learning:
■ Undertaken to prepare 'newcomers' to practice ■ Uses a range of placements ■ A key feature of pre-registration healthcare programmes ■ Professional regulatory bodies may determine the proportion of time (including the minimum number of hours) that students are required to complete as part of a pre-registration healthcare programme ■ Professional regulatory bodies may have specific guidance regarding the role of mentors	■ Learners are usually employees ■ Learners are required to balance their role as a learner and a worker ■ Learning occurs while working ■ Learning and working are coincident ■ A key feature of specific programmes such as the Foundation degree award ■ Requires the support of employers and managers ■ May be undertaken to address workforce needs, e.g. the development of new roles such as the assistant practitioner or senior support worker role

Activity 2 will have helped you to make sense of practice-based learning and work-based learning and to identify the similarities and differences (see *Table 1.1*). Sarbjit and Dave both have experience on which to base their new learning, having worked in health and social care prior to commencing their respective programmes of study. They have both engaged in 'learning by doing', also known as experiential learning, and this has been supported by their mentors. Sarbjit's mentor Mandy and Dave's mentor Kate have spent time encouraging their mentees to engage in reflection. For Dave it was reflecting on the care that he had given to make sense of the requirement to escalate his concerns should he be faced with a situation where standards of care have been compromised. For Sarbjit this meant writing a reflection piece in order to make sense of an experience that was new, powerful and upsetting. Her engagement in reflection was as much about understanding her feelings and emotions as her actions during the cardiac arrest situation. Spouse (2001) observes that practitioners with limited knowledge or understanding of their environment may find that everything appears as a blur of activity. Sarbjit therefore needed to engage in reflection in a deeper way than Dave, who is already familiar with his clinical area. On the surface Dave's lack of knowledge of his trust's escalating concerns procedure came from Kate's questioning approach, although after further discussion Dave was able to recall a situation that occurred some months earlier where he acted in response to concerns he had regarding the care of a patient. For Dave, therefore, engaging in reflection and identifying his learning needs led him to 'reframe' his existing knowledge and understand the standard of work required by his employer – namely that band 4 senior support workers or assistant practitioners must demonstrate their knowledge and understanding of whistle-blowing and the trust policy on escalating concerns.

You will have seen that as a practice-based learner Sarbjit is on placement and being prepared for practice that involves exposure to a range of new and challenging experiences while becoming part of a new community of practice – the urology ward's nursing team. Dave is already in practice and has been a member of his community of practice for a number of years. While he knows certain aspects of his job role well, he lacks underpinning knowledge in key areas that is necessary if he is to make the transition to his new role as an assistant practitioner. Additionally, Dave has to balance fulfilling his current role as a rehabilitation assistant with attending university, studying, and using his workplace for learning while preparing for his new role.

Summary

In this first chapter we have explored the importance of learning and its relationship to change. We have discussed the difference between knowledge, information and understanding and what it means to be in practice and to practise within health and social care settings. Although practice-based and work-based learning appear to be similar, there are key differences associated with the context and purpose in which the learning takes place. Both types of learning require a range of knowledge, skills and strategies that will be explored in greater detail in the remainder of this book. In Chapter 2 we will focus on the context in which work-based learning occurs by exploring being at work, what it means to work for an organisation, and how organisations operate.

Key points

- Questioning is a useful approach used by teachers to uncover assumptions, beliefs, values and hidden knowledge within learners
- The evidence that learning has taken place is when your behaviour changes
- Understanding is demonstrated when you can provide an explanation not only for your actions but for the course of action that you have taken based on your knowledge
- Information is readily available but is not the same as knowledge that is required in order to practise
- Practice-based learning is used to prepare learners for practice using a wide range of clinical and therapeutic placements ahead of registration with a professional body
- Work-based learning uses work and the workplace to aid learning: it requires employees to balance the demands of fulfilling the role that they have been employed for, while also working and gaining the learning they need to develop their professional practice

- Practice-based and work-based learners may be supported by workplace mentors, who will be required to provide a range of skills that include: debriefing following challenging situations, assessing a learner's competency, skills and knowledge, and reflection in and on practice events
- Practice-based learning within particular professions such as nursing is characterised as education by and for a distinct professional group whereas work-based learning is education that is orientated to standards of work associated with organisational requirements in general and the specific team or place of work where the work-based learner is situated.

Useful websites

- Assistant Practitioners: www.assistantpractitioners.co.uk/
- Health and Care Professionals Council: www.hcpc-uk.org
- Nursing and Midwifery Council: www.nmc.org.uk
- Skills for Care: www.skillsforcare.org.uk
- Skills for Health: www.skillsforhealth.org.uk
- Royal College of Nursing student community: www.rcn.org.uk/ development/students
- Royal College of Nursing – roles of healthcare assistants and assistant practitioners: www.rcn.org.uk/nursing/work_in_health_care/become_a_ health_care_assistant www.rcn.org.uk/nursing/work_in_health_care/ become_an_assistant_practitioner
- Using reflection during practice-based learning: www.reading.ac.uk/ internal/studyadvice/StudyResources/sta-practicebasedlearning.aspx

Interesting blogs

- www.assistantpractitioners.co.uk/forum-2/
- https://notanotherstudentnurse.wordpress.com
- http://britainsnurses.co.uk
- www.health.org.uk

References

Billett S (2004) Learning through work – workplace participatory practices. In: Rainbird H, Fuller A, Munro A, eds. *Workplace Learning in Context*. Routledge, London: 109–25

Boud D, Solomon N (2001) *Work-based Learning – a New Higher Education?* SRHE/Open University Press, Buckingham

Burnard P (2002) *Learning Human Skills – an Experiential and Reflective Guide for Nurses and Health Care Professionals*. 4th edn. Butterworth-Heinemann, Oxford

Cronin C (2014) Workplace learning – a healthcare perspective. *Education & Training* **56:** 329–42

Eraut M (2000) Non-formal learning and tacit knowledge in professional work. *British Journal of Educational Psychology* **70:** 113–36

Eraut M (2004) Informal learning in the workplace. *Studies in Continuing Education* **26:** 247–73

Kilgallon K, Thompson J, eds (2012) *Mentoring in Nursing and Healthcare: a Practical Approach*. Wiley-Blackwell, Oxford

Lave J, Wenger E (1991) *Situated Learning: Legitimate Peripheral Participation*. Cambridge University Press, Cambridge

Nettleton R (2013) Practice-based learning, but not as we know it: lessons from improvising advanced practice roles. *International Journal of Practice-based Learning in Health and Social Care* **1:** 63–76

Oxford Dictionary of English (2005) *Oxford Dictionary of English*. 2nd edn. Oxford University Press, Oxford

Price B (2012) Key principles in assessing students' practice-based learning. *Nurs Stand* **26:** 49–55

Raelin JA (2008) *Work-based Learning: Bridging Knowledge and Action in the Workplace*. Jossey-Bass, San Francisco

Rogoff B (1995) Observing sociocultural activity on three planes: participatory appropriation, guided participation and apprenticeship. In: Wertsch JV, Del Rio P, Alvarez A, eds. *Sociocultural Studies of Mind*. Cambridge University Press, Cambridge: 139–63

Spouse J (2001) Work-based learning in health care environments. *Nurse Educ Pract* **1:** 12–18

Thistlethwaite J (2013) Practice-based learning across and between the health professions: a conceptual exploration of definitions and diversity and their impact on interprofessional education. *International Journal of Practice-based Learning in Health and Social Care* **1**: 15–28

Wareing M (2012) Rhetoric and reality: the theoretical basis of work-based learning and the lived experience of the Foundation degree student. Open University, unpublished EdD Thesis

Williams C (2010) Understanding the essential elements of work-based learning and its relevance to everyday clinical practice. *J Nurs Manage* **18**: 624–32

CHAPTER 2

Being at work and working for an organisation

By the end of this chapter you will be able to:

1. Define work and its key features
2. Explain the importance of motivation
3. Discuss the key features of organisations and why change is necessary.

Introduction

In Chapter 1 we began by exploring the concept of learning and making the distinction between knowledge, information and understanding. The two vignettes featuring Sarbjit and Dave helped you to make sense of the difference between practice-based and work-based learning. In this chapter you will explore the nature of work and what it means to work within an organisation; a topic that is of relevance to all learners.

Activity 3

Try and think about what work means to you and reflect on:
■ What the costs and benefits of work are for you
■ What factors have an impact on your motivation as a worker
■ What work requires of you.

This first activity will have led to some mixed feelings! It could be argued that there are two features that characterise working in health and social care – that you can only be certain of constant uncertainty, and that what does not change is the presence of change. Sadly, the act of caring for people has been seen by some work-based learners as a barrier to learning (Wareing, 2012). It is therefore vital to understand the nature of work and your attitude to it if you are to use the workplace for learning.

What is work?

The sociologist Anthony Giddens (1993) described work has having the following characteristics:

- *Money:* You work in order to receive money that can be used to sustain your life, provide for yourself and any dependents that you have.
- *Activity level:* Work requires you to engage in activities that you are capable of undertaking based on the experience that you have accrued and the knowledge and skills that you have acquired and bring to the employment market place and make you employable.
- *Variety:* The range of activities engaged in at work will determine the levels of reward in terms of personal satisfaction and, arguably, the degree of payment in wages you receive.
- *Temporal structure:* Your work is temporal because it must be commenced and completed within specific timeframes set by the opening times of your workplace, the time in which work must be completed and when it is most desirable to engage in specific activities based on safety, performance and productivity. Naturally, within health and social care settings, care is often delivered throughout a 24-hour cycle, with levels of activity being determined by the needs of the client. Often the availability of the healthcare worker is determined by the roster or 'off-duty', a phrase suggesting that the absence of the healthcare worker is of greater significance than his or her presence.
- *Social contact:* A key feature of work in health and social care working environments is the unparalleled opportunity for social contact that such employment affords. Work provides you with an opportunity to have long and deep associations with like-minded co-workers despite the diversity of you and your colleagues' social backgrounds.

■ *Personal identity:* Working in health and social care requires you to subscribe to a particular set of values with regard to the dignity and personhood of service users, which suggests that such work is morally virtuous. Put more simply, the nature of your employment determines not only the role you fulfil within society but how society values and rewards the contribution you make, although the degree of value and reward in terms of salary may differ. In fact, voluntary work is often greatly valued by society and yet is characterised by its status as unpaid work.

Activity 4

■ With regard to working in professional practice environments, are there any additional characteristics that could be added to this list?
■ Look up the word 'vocation' in a dictionary and think about whether you see your work as vocational, and if so why?

The meaning of work

Activity 4 will have helped you undercover some characteristics that make working in health and social care unique and help explain why it provides a high level of personal satisfaction despite its many challenges. The word 'vocation' is interesting and is often applied to areas of employment that require person-centred skills, although its original usage was associated with the church and people being 'called' into religious service that was spiritually-governed work rather than a career. Although our society has become more secular, with religious institutions having lost some of their influence, we can recover the idea of vocational work by differentiating work from labour. The 20th century philosopher Hannah Arendt (1958) described labour, work and craft as key characteristics of the human condition and observed that work is often referred to as 'the labour of life' that positions human beings within the world and that work is worldliness. Arendt argued that every occupation has had to prove that it is useful to society at large and that work rather than labour authenticates human activity. Jarvis (2009) developed this idea further by describing the concept of 'becoming', where learning and our progress through stages of the lifecycle enable us to become and shape our sense of self or our 'personhood'.

Activity 5

Think about:

■ Where you see yourself within the life cycle.

■ What life transitions have been significant for you and why?

■ What aspects of your life history have been most important to you and how they are shaping your learning now?

Activity 5 will have helped you to realise that there is a strong relationship between the work that you engage in at different stages of your life and how your identity is shaped and formed by the learning opportunities that employment (whether paid of unpaid) affords you. Jarvis (2009) argues that our 'becoming' is about lifelong learning, as this type of learning develops and transforms us through our engagement with the world so that we fulfil our human potential.

Having explored the concept of 'becoming' and how you learn inwardly, you also need to consider what it means to fulfil a professional role and how the activities and tools that you use in working environments shape your identities outwardly. The concept of 'being' is concerned with how your learning within the world leads you to develop new identities before the world. In Chapter 1 we considered Sarbjit, a nursing student on her first ward. In order to make sense of how identity is shaped in learning situations we will return to Sarbjit as illustrated in Vignette 3.

Jarvis (2009) describes how learning shapes our identities in terms of the identity that is ascribed to us as a novice. Our identity emerges from exposure to a range of experiences. When sufficient skills have been gained or achieved we become established in our new role. Sarbjit is a new nursing student and is little-by-little experiencing being a nurse, although she is a student. She arrives on placement having donned her uniform, which signifies that she is a nursing student; but in essence her patients regard her as a nurse, as illustrated in Vignette 3. Therefore, although she is not a fully qualified registered nurse, her identity as a nurse has been ascribed to her. Mandy has achieved her identity as a fully qualified staff nurse and is able to act as a workplace mentor by virtue of her experience, qualifications, job description and employment. When Mandy sits down to read Sarbjit's reflection piece she will be able to explain to Sarbjit how to field questions from patients, relatives and other visitors during a cardiac arrest situation in such a way as to reassure them while protecting the dignity and privacy of the patient. The identities of Sarbjit and

Dave appear to be different, although the nature of their identities and the end to which their learning will allow them to become professionals is quite similar, as they will achieve their new identities as a fully qualified staff nurse and assistant practitioner as they gain expertise. Jarvis (2009) observes that in each role we play we learn not only to perform that role but learn how to be it.

The process of becoming and being that occurs within workplaces is associated not only with whom you work with, but what you work with. You will recall from Chapter 1 that work-based learning is learning that is acquired in the midst of action. Heidegger (1977) described how the meaning of work is characterised by the tools that are used, in the sense that a tool within the workplace is something that is 'ready-to-hand'. In Vignette 3 we saw that Sarbjit wondered whether there was anything that she could have done with regards to

Vignette 3: Sarbjit reflecting on a challenging incident

Following a difficult shift where Sarbjit had experienced her first cardiac arrest while working alongside Mandy her mentor, Sarbjit returned home and sat down to write a reflection piece as advised by Mandy. After a few minutes of staring at the screen of her iPad, Sarbjit decided to describe what had happened by recalling the events that had led to her patient collapsing and the crash team being called in response.

The events of the day were very clear in Sarbjit's mind and she had no difficulty describing her feelings and what went well and not so well. One of things that Sarbjit realised when analysing the situation was how helpless she felt towards her patient. Although she felt pleased that she had been able to observe what went on during the cardiac arrest, albeit at a safe distance, Sarbjit wondered whether there should have been something she could have done with regards to the cardiac arrest trolley or whether she could have reassured nearby patients and visitors. In fact, while the patient was being resuscitated a patient's relative had approached Sarbjit and said: 'Excuse me nurse, is he going to be alright?' Sarbjit felt awkward being addressed as a nurse within earshot of her colleagues and had not known how to respond. Although Sarbjit was too tired to complete her reflection piece, she decided to take what she had done into work to discuss it with Mandy, as she felt she needed advice on how best to support, reassure and counsel other patients and relatives following a cardiac arrest.

the cardiac arrest trolley, which demonstrates that tools within the workplace – like artefacts in a museum – are objects that possess significance and meaning. When tools or pieces of equipment break down, time literally 'stands still' and a worker is rendered inactive. This is another example of the temporality or 'time-centredness' of working environments that we explored earlier.

Working for an organisation

We started this chapter with an activity that required you to reflect on what factors have an impact on your motivation as a worker, or why people bother to turn up for work. Mullins (2013) provides three explanations that orientate people's attitude to working within an organisation:

1. 'Work is a means to an end': This approach is referred to as the instrumental orientation or, more simply, activities are either related to work or are non-work related. People who hold an instrumental attitude view work as a demeaning necessity.
2. 'Work is central to my life': This orientation to work is called bureaucratic, as workers feel they have an obligation to their organisation because they have a commitment to their career. Work is therefore an activity that links both.
3. 'Work is about me and my team': This approach is about the solidarity that orientates a worker, in the sense that even activities done outside of work are linked to work and their relationships with other workers.

Your behaviour towards your organisation is based on the expectation that the completion of work will be both rewarding, in terms of your personal or intrinsic satisfaction, and rewarded through a salary and other benefits in kind. Handy (1993) argues that workers' motivation is driven by the satisfaction of being productive and the incentives provided by employers that drive performance, which may include 'sticks' as well as 'carrots'. The psychologist Richard Gross (2005) argued that in order to perform and be productive at work you are required to:

■ *Be attentive:* This requires you to focus your attention in order to process and filter information

- *Recognise patterns:* Make decisions based on the recognition of patterns such as similarities and differences
- *Use your perception:* To use your thinking and cognitive ability to reason, order and prioritise
- *Memorise:* By drawing on your personal knowledge or knowledge that is particular to your department or organisation
- *Use language:* By using appropriate professional terminology
- *Solve problems:* By working in collaboration and forming partnerships with people while using resources, tools and equipment
- *Be 'pro-social':* Possess a genuine desire to work for and with people and place the needs of others above your own by acting in an altruistic manner
- *Conform:* By coming under the influence of the group, team or organisation and acting in obedience in order to meet standards of work while conforming to the mission statement.

Organisational change

You will recall from Chapter 1 that the greatest evidence that learning has occurred is when your behaviour changes. Change within health and social care organisations is not only ever-present and constant, but is vital to prevent client and patient care becoming stagnant. Sale (2005) argues that within health and social care there is a strong relationship between the willingness to change and the culture of organisations. Change is a process that is levered by changes in health policy, the introduction of new technology, or changing demographics such as the rising number of over 65-year-olds with long-term conditions. Change can also be triggered by circumstances and pressures that come from the grass roots of an organisation; these are changes that are triggered from the 'bottom-up' as well as 'top-down' and can arise from changes in law or from the government or can be triggered at executive or board level. There are many models of change that seek to explain each stage of the change process. Broadly, however, the process of change within organisations occurs when:

- People act rationally in accordance with their own interests where change is seen to be justified and beneficial to them. This is called an empirical rational approach.

- People act according to social 'norms' or what is acceptable or customary based on their attitudes, beliefs and intelligence. This is called a normative re-educative approach.
- Change arises from conflict, where dissatisfaction and frustration leads to the identification of a resolution that results in change. This is termed the power coercive approach to change.

(Mullins, 2013)

Activity 6

Think about a change that has occurred in an organisation that you are involved or familiar with:
- What were the triggers and drivers for the change?
- How did people respond to the change?
- Was there any resistance to the change; if so why, and if not why not?

Summary

In this chapter we have explored the characteristics of work and what motivates our attitude towards the organisation that employs us. Learning occurs within all stages of the life cycle and shapes your identity as you gain knowledge and skills and develop new ways of working. Exposure to new experiences is the key to workplace learning and can enable learners, such as Sarbjit, to realise the significance and meaning associated with tools. Your productivity at work is reliant not only on working conditions but a range of personal attributes and cognitive abilities that need to develop through lifelong learning so that you can cope with the constant change and uncertainty that characterises health and social care organisations.

Key points

- Money, the level and variety of activity, and the personal satisfaction gained from work are as important as the reward arising from the completion of work
- As a worker you are required to have a range of knowledge, skills and personal attributes that shape your motivation towards and engagement in work
- Change in health and social care is constant, normal and essential in preventing care from becoming stagnant
- Organisations have to manage and plan for change carefully
- You are not necessarily the target for change but your knowledge, attitudes and behaviour should change in response to learning.

Useful websites

- Department of Health: www.gov.uk/government/organisations/department-of-health
- Healthcare UK: www.gov.uk/government/organisations/healthcare-uk
- Health Emergency: www.healthemergency.org.uk
- Public Concern at Work: www.pcaw.org.uk
- The King's Fund: www.kingsfund.org.uk
- The Work Foundation: www.theworkfoundation.com
- Unison: www.unison.org.uk

References

Arendt H (1958) *The Human Condition.* 2nd edn. University of Chicago Press, Chicago

Giddens A (1993) *Sociology.* 2nd edn. Polity Press, Cambridge

Gross R (2005) *Psychology: the Science of Mind and Behaviour.* 5th edn. Hodder, Harlow

Handy C (1993) *Understanding Organizations*. 4th edn. Penguin, London

Heidegger M (1977) *The Question Concerning Technology and Other Essays*. Harper, New York

Jarvis P (2009) *Learning to be a Person in Society*. Routledge, London

Mullins LJ (2013) *Management and Organisational Behaviour*. 10th edn. Pearson, Harlow

Sale D (2005) *Understanding Clinical Governance and Quality Assurance: Making it Happen*. Palgrave, Basingstoke

Wareing M (2012) Rhetoric and reality: the theoretical basis of work-based learning and the lived experience of the Foundation degree student. Open University, unpublished EdD Thesis

CHAPTER 3

Using the Me, My, More, Must approach to learning

By the end of this chapter you will be able to:

1. Identify a range of values that should underpin your practice
2. Explain each stage of the Me, My, More, Must approach
3. Analyse the use of reflection to make sense of how values impact on practice.

Introduction

In this chapter we will explore the importance of professionalism and how values and beliefs can impact on your practice. You will also be introduced to a completely new approach to learning through reflection called the Me, My, More, Must model.

Reflection

In Chapter 1 we looked at the importance of reflection as a strategy for learning from experience. This form of learning is called 'experiential learning'. We saw that while every situation is a potential learning situation, we do not necessarily learn from everything we do and that we need to 'notice' not only what is happening but to 'notice ourselves'. Reflection is a tool to help us learn by noticing what is happening around us by looking within ourselves to identify what we are thinking and feeling. Almost all of the vignettes in this book depict incidents that require Dave and Sarbjit to reflect, and so we will start by exploring what it means to be a reflective learner in health and social care settings.

Reflection and reflective writing started to influence nursing and professional education in the early 1990s (Atkins and Murphy, 1993) and was heavily influenced by the work of Donald Schön, who described the crisis of confidence that professionals experience when there is a mismatch between their knowledge and the uncertainty and instability that occurs in practice situations (Schön, 2003).

In Chapter 2, we explored the nature of change and uncertainty. Modern working life has become characterised by 'supercomplexity', which according to Frost (2010) is shaped by:

- Increasing globalisation, where professionals and professionalism have a worldwide reference point
- An explosion in the availability and dissemination of information and the development of a networked society, where professionals can no longer practise in isolation
- The rise of risk management and the need to audit workplace activity and the use of resources.

Frost (2010) concludes that these three areas have left professionals feeling pressured, as they feel they have lost control of their practise while their work is being constantly scrutinised. Consequently, lifelong learning is essential in order to manage risk, evaluate the use of resources and make sense of the large volume of information that influences organisations. As a result, workers have to develop particular capabilities, such as learning through reflection, rather than be reliant on previous experience and old ways of working.

Background to the Me, My, More, Must approach

I developed the Me, My, More, Must approach having been influenced by the findings of the Francis Report (2013), a public inquiry led by Sir Robert Francis QC that uncovered poor standards of care and high mortality rates at Stafford Hospital. As someone who worked for the NHS for many years, I reflected on how I would have responded to the working conditions at Stafford Hospital and how working in the NHS has shaped who I am as a professional. Roberts and Ion (2014) have highlighted the dangers of thoughtlessness, where healthcare practitioners fail to use their intellect to reason and reflect in a critical manner as a significant factor in the 'moral catastrophes' that occurred at Stafford and Winterbourne View Private Hospital, where residents with learning disabilities were abused by care staff. The phrase 'moral catastrophe' is a powerful but useful term as it helps us to focus on our conduct and the values that shape our role, practice and patient care.

Values in health and social care

Part of the government response (Department of Health, 2013) to the findings of the Francis Report was to initiate a review of patient safety within the NHS. The Berwick Review (2013) recommended the promotion of a culture of learning throughout all areas of the NHS. While learning is important, the impact of values held by staff at Stafford and Winterbourne View Hospitals was of even greater significance as it determined the quality of care that patients received. Kozier et al (2007, p. 40) state that values are our personal beliefs and attitudes about a person, object, idea or action; whereas a value set is the small group of values held by us as individuals. We organise our set of values internally along a continuum from the most important to the least important, and this forms a value system. Each value system is held together by beliefs that are assumptions we accept as being true and that shape our attitudes, which in turn determine our way of thinking, behaving and feeling.

Activity 7

■ Identify your own values and beliefs – make a list.
■ What are the origins of your own values and beliefs?
■ What sort of workplace situations do you find yourself in which are at odds with your own values and beliefs?

A key characteristic of caregiving is altruism, or the 'giving of oneself'. Being altruistic or 'pro-social' requires you to possess a genuine desire to place the

Table 3.1 The Me, My, More, Must approach

Stage	Writing prompts
Me	■ Who am I? ■ What values are important to me as a person? ■ What values are important to me as a healthcare worker? ■ What do I need in order to feel confident at work? ■ What decreases my confidence at work? ■ What enables me to be able to practise effectively in a clinical or therapeutic area? ■ What prevents me from practising effectively in a clinical or therapeutic area?
My	■ What are my thoughts and feelings regarding this learning experience, situation or incident? ■ What concerns do I have regarding myself? ■ What concerns do I have about other people involved in this experience? ■ Who can help me make sense of this experience or situation? ■ What impact have my values had on the people involved in this experience? ■ What impact has my level of confidence had on how I have practised during this experience? ■ In general, what have I learnt from this experience, situation or incident?
More	■ What questions have been generated from this experience, situation or incident? ■ What ideas have been generated from this experience, situation or incident? ■ What has surprised or puzzled me about this experience, situation or incident? ■ What do I need to find more information about as a result of this experience, situation or incident?
Must	■ What must I do now to identify my learning needs? ■ What must I do to identify my learning goals? ■ Who must I speak to, to assist me in creating a learning or development plan? ■ What must I include in the plan? ■ What values must I explore in order to become the healthcare worker I wish to become?

needs of others above your own. The key values that characterise practice in health and social care include compassion (being active with regard for another person's welfare); empathy (the ability to see someone else's perspective or lived experience and convey an identification with it); discernment (being able to make decisions with sensitive insight); trustworthiness (being reliable, having a good moral character and being competent); integrity (maintaining and sustaining 'best practice' and being willing to stand on principle); and conscientiousness (doing the right thing, considering the right action, for example truth telling). In order to reflect on your practice it is important to be conscious of the impact that your values have on your care giving (Kozier, et al, 2007).

There are many models of reflection that have sought to help learners to reflect and write pieces of reflection. Many of these frameworks require learners to start by reflecting on a specific experience, incident or situation (e.g. Kolb, 1984; Boud et al, 1985; Gibbs, 1988; Driscoll, 2006). My approach, in contrast, requires you to start the process of reflection with a consideration of who you are. You will be exploring the importance of developing self-awareness in relation to the nature of who you are in Chapter 7, when you will consider the nature of authentic professional practice. *Table 3.1* presents the Me, My, More, Must approach with a selection of writing prompts to assist you to think and write reflectively.

In order to make sense of the Me, My, More, Must model, I have written a short piece of reflection (*Box 3.1*) that explores my own values and how they have shaped the professional I think I have become.

I realised from writing my piece of reflection that our professional and clinical identities are never static but shaped by a range of 'triggers' and 'drivers'. While the Francis Report (2013) triggered me to think about how I would have acted if I had been in the same situation as staff at Stafford Hospital, one of the key drivers for a re-evaluation of my professional identity was the prospect of moving to a new post in a completely new organisation. While triggers and drivers stimulate reflection, the Me, My, More, Must approach has been designed to help you consider who you are and what impact your values might have before a description of the particular experience, situation or incident that you wish to use as the focus of your reflective writing. In the next section we will explore how you can use the approach within clinical and therapeutic settings and in formal learning situations. We will now return to Sarbjit and explore how she used the Me, My, More, Must approach during her most recent clinical placement.

Box 3.1: Reflection piece

Me

■ Who am I?
■ What values are important to me as a person?
■ What values are important to me as a healthcare worker?

My parents were members of the Salvation Army, a Christian church established in Victorian London whose 'soldiers and officers' are characterised by their practical demonstration of service, self-denial and evangelical worship featuring brass bands. Following my three older brothers, I attended 'the Citadel' and as a teenager came under the influence of a Salvation Army officer who had previously trained and practised as a nurse in South Wales. Keith was and is a kind, gentle and Godly family man who had the ability to make older people feel special while demonstrating unfailing patience and interest in a group of teenagers that included me. I was a decathlon member of the Salvation Army. It was my second home and my friends, members of the band and the many non-uniformed members (who included a large number of elderly folk) were my extended family. My teens comprised of endless band practices, open-air meetings and helping out with jumble sales. Each Christmas day was spent helping to feed and entertain the elderly, vulnerable and lonely who could be found each day in our local shopping centre. At 17 I rebelled and went in search of a new charismatic church 'experience' a year before leaving home to start my nurse training in Birmingham.

My

■ What are my thoughts and feelings regarding this learning experience, situation or incident?
■ What concerns do I have regarding myself?
■ What concerns do I have about other people involved in this experience?

Now that I am in my mid-forties I see that those early years were not only formative but unique and transformational. One of the key values that the Salvation Army taught me – and that was captured in its controversial strap line 'For Christ's sake care' – is that 'people need you as much as you need them'. When I entered nursing it was explained to us that we were unlikely to change the world, but that it was possible for us to change someone's world and that essential nursing care (washing, bathing, mobilising, feeding, making patients comfortable and comforting patients) would be the vehicle to the establishment of a caring relationship that is essential to healing.

More
■ What questions have been generated from this experience, situation or incident?
■ What ideas have been generated from this experience, situation or incident?
■ What has surprised or puzzled me about this experience, situation or incident?

This morning I am sitting at home in the small box bedroom that I pretentiously refer to as 'my study'. I am trying to write the third chapter of my first book and struggling to say something new about 'reflection', a word my students groan at and a topic that has been covered by academics with far greater credibility than me. Out of the window I see our jolly postman, circling the close in his red puffer jacket on this cold February morning. I pop downstairs and open an envelope from an international organisation that I support each month with a small donation. Its latest newsletter describes the poverty, fear and loneliness of people in the Middle East, central Africa and the Indian sub-continent, who like me are Christians, but are persecuted for their faith. I reflect on the distance that has grown between me and those needy folks I met years ago at those Salvation Army jumble sales and coffee mornings and my current role as a university teacher. The only visits I make to clinical areas now are to meet students and staff. While I am thankful for an interesting and varied career, I cannot help but wonder about what I have lost. Are my current professional values at odds with those that I held as a nursing student? Has my identity as a teacher and my interest in education distanced me from really caring and being compassionate? Has the loss of my clinical credibility led to an erosion of those fundamental values that led me to pursue a vocational career?

Must
■ What must I do now to identify my learning needs?
■ What must I do to identify my learning goals?
■ What values must I explore in order to become the healthcare worker I wish to become?

In a few months' time I will be starting a new job in a different university. I will be joining a new team and working in a region of England that is largely unfamiliar to me. My new job has more seniority and I will be required to demonstrate leadership and fulfil management responsibilities. I will also have to spend 1 day per month working in a clinical environment. I have realised that I need to look at my behaviours and explore how I can become a skilled influencer. What is it about me that has been useful in my current job, but which may not be appropriate in my new post? How will I cope with less student contact and will the loss of contact be similar to the experience I had when I left clinical nursing to enter education? What will be the costs and how can I minimise them so that I do not lose sight of the needs of my students and my responsibility for their practice learning? How can I ensure that working one shift a month in a clinical area is a meaningful learning experience? These questions have an authentic feel and I will explore them further with my new mentor so that I can create a new identity for myself; an identity that is rooted in those formative years, shaped by the past and fit for the future.

Vignette 4: Sarbjit using the Me, My, More, Must approach in practice

At the start of her final year Sarbjit was given the opportunity to undertake a short 2-week placement at an inner city shelter for the homeless run by a not-for-profit organisation. On her first morning Sarbjit helped serve breakfast and was introduced to Carmel, a 38-year-old woman who had been using the shelter for the past 10 days. Sarbjit sat and had a coffee with Carmel and learnt that she had grown up in a rural farming community in Suffolk, loved horses and spent 15 years in the British Army. Carmel had found the adjustment to civilian life difficult and had struggled to find satisfying employment. Carmel became quite tearful with Sarbjit when she explained that she had developed panic attacks, which had led to sleeplessness and a lack of confidence. As a result she lost her job as a supervisor in a warehouse a month before the tenancy on her flat came to end.

Later that evening Sarbjit wrote a piece of reflection using the Me, My, More, Must approach. Although Sarbjit was aware that ex-service personnel do sometimes become homeless, she was surprised that someone such as Carmel – who had been so open and articulate – had 'ended-up' in a shelter for the homeless. Sarbjit started her reflection by identifying her own values and compared her upbringing with Carmel's.

Sarbjit's father had served in the Navy as an engineer, but had left the armed forces to become a maths teacher, having studied for a degree via distance learning. Sarbjit thought about her own upbringing, growing up in an industrial new town, and compared it with Carmel's seemingly idyllic childhood in East Anglia. Sarbjit was puzzled that Carmel had found adjusting to life outside the forces difficult and then realised the impact her own beliefs and value system was having on her perception of Carmel.

She realised that she had assumed that all ex-service personnel were like her father, in the sense of being strong, motivated and independent. Sarbjit had been impressed with her father's determination to study while serving with the Navy, and this had influenced Sarbjit's decision to go to university. Sarbjit reflected on her own assumptions regarding Carmel's social background, and whether growing up in rural Suffolk had provided her with the same life chances and choices that Sarbjit had been given with regard to the access to further education that had helped Sarbjit secure a place at university. She thought about her two older brothers, who had been able to complete apprenticeships with large multinational companies located in the town she grew up in. Sarbjit also reflected on the influence of her aunt, a physiotherapist who had encouraged her to pursue her dream of going to university and to have a career in the NHS. Sarbjit realised that alongside the influence of her father, her aunt had been a strong role model and mentor.

Sarbjit resolved to try and get to know Carmel better, should Carmel feel comfortable talking to her again. Sarbjit had been surprised by her preconceived ideas regarding homeless people and service personnel, and was shocked that a constellation of circumstances could easily lead to someone using a shelter. Sarbjit decided to research the needs of former service personnel and realised that she had little understanding of common emotional disorders such as panic attacks and anxiety-related conditions. She also resolved to discuss Carmel's care with her key worker, who Sarbjit had met briefly on her first day, as she had not worked with a key worker before.

Vignette 4 has demonstrated how the Me, My, More, Must approach has been useful in uncovering the preconceived ideas held by Sarbjit with regard to the social background, life choices and circumstances of a vulnerable service user. A placement in a social care setting has already proved to be a valuable learning opportunity for Sarbjit, who has been able to identify the power of her own life experience and the influence of family members on the shape of her value system, which has been challenged by her encounter with Carmel.

Sarbjit realised that she needed to build a deeper relationship with Carmel in order to obtain a clearer picture of her circumstances and needs. She also realised that she should research anxiety-related disorders and the role of key workers in social care.

Using the approach in formal learning

The Me, My, More, Must approach can be adapted for use in formal learning situations such as taught sessions at university or even training and study days. I have used the approach with my own students to enable them to use the model to engage in 'reflection-in-action' while in class.

Figure 3.1 was developed for a session that I delivered on academic writing and Harvard referencing. The notes sheet has proved useful as it enables students to identify their initial thoughts and feelings, what they have learnt from the session, and to capture any ideas or questions as they come to mind while engaging in learning in a formal setting. You can adapt the notes sheet in *Figure 3.1* to your own learning circumstances. Consider photocopying it or drawing your own version to use during training or to reflect on learning experiences.

In simple terms, the Me, My, More, Must approach seeks to enable you to explore who you are as a health and social practitioner as well as a learner before making sense of a learning experience so that your values are at the forefront of your practice-based and work-based learning experiences. I believe the approach is important for learners like Dave and Sarbjit, who are developing their professional identities while participating in learning within different clinical and therapeutic settings.

Summary

In this chapter we have returned to the topic of reflection, which we have explored from the perspective of reflecting in order to notice ourselves. This is important because you need to identify not only your own personal beliefs and values, but the impact they have on your practice. In doing so you will not

Figure 3.1. Me, My, More, Must notes sheet for a session on academic writing and Harvard referencing

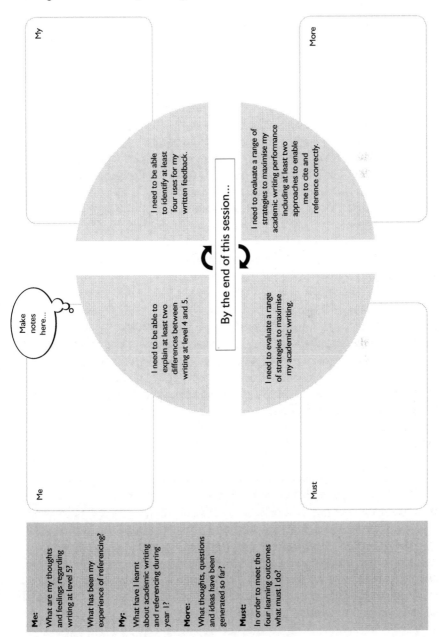

only learn from experiences, situations and incidents, but determine the kind of professional you wish to become.

The challenges that professionals face that have led to the adoption of reflection to help practitioners' manage constant change, uncertainty and supercomplexity are still with us. The impact of the Francis Report and the investigation into Winterbourne Hospital have led some commentators to refer to such cases as 'moral catastrophes'. Questions have been raised about the ability of health and social care workers to think and reason in such situations. It is therefore important that you explore the origin of your values and the impact that they have on your practise. This is particularly important when you are using clinical and therapeutic workplaces for learning and when your professional identity is being shaped by learning experiences, situations and incidents that arise from practice. The Me, My, More, Must approach is a model of reflection that requires you to consider the impact of your beliefs and value system, and is sufficiently flexible to be used in formal learning situations.

Key points

- Healthcare professionals need to become reflective practitioners in order to deal with the large volume of information and evidence that underpins practice and the challenge of working within modern organisations that are characterised by constant change, uncertainty and supercomplexity
- Organisations require workers to develop particular capabilities, such as learning through reflection, rather than be reliant on previous experience and old ways of working
- High-profile cases that have revealed failures in care have been described as moral catastrophes and have led to recommendations for the promotion of learning organisations; this requires all health and social care workers to think, reason and reflect on their practice
- Values are your personal beliefs and attitudes about a person, object, idea or action, while a value set is the small group of values you hold
- People organise their set of values internally along a continuum from most to least important
- Each value system is held together by beliefs, which are assumptions that you accept as being true and that shape your attitudes and determine your way of thinking, behaving and feeling

- The key characteristics of caregiving are the giving of oneself by being altruistic, compassionate, showing empathy, exercising discernment, being trustworthy and demonstrating integrity and conscientiousness.
- The Me, My, More, Must approach is a reflective model that requires you to ask who you are; what thoughts and feelings you have regarding a learning experience, situation or incident; what you need to find more information about as a result; and what values you must explore in order to become the professional you wish to become.

Useful websites

- Driscoll model of reflection: www.nottingham.ac.uk/nmp/sonet/rlos/ placs/critical_reflection/models/driscoll.html
- Gibbs model of reflection: www.brookes.ac.uk/students/upgrade/study-skills/reflective-writing-gibbs/
- Johns model of reflection: http://skillsforlearning.leedsbeckett.ac.uk/ preview/content/models/04.shtml
- Kolb model of reflection: http://mycourse.solent.ac.uk/mod/book/view. php?id=2732&chapterid=1112
- Reflective writing log examples: www.wlv.ac.uk/about-us/internal-departments/centre-for-lifelong-learning/research-and-development/ historians-reflect/how-to-reflect/

References

Atkins S, Murphy K (1993) Reflection: a review of the literature. *J Adv Nurs* **18:** 1188–92

Berwick D, National Advisory Group on the Safety of Patients in England (2013) A Promise to Learn – a Commitment to Act: Improving the Safety of Patients in England. Department of Health. www.gov.uk/government/ publications/berwick-review-into-patient-safety (accessed 4 November 2015)

Boud D, Keogh R, Walker D, eds (1985) *Reflection: Turning Experience into Learning*. Kogan Page, London

Department of Health (2013) Patients First and Foremost: the Initial Government Response to the Report of the Mid-Staffordshire NHS Foundation Trust Public Inquiry. www.gov.uk/government/publications/government-initial-response-to-the-mid-staffs-report (accessed 4 November 2015)

Driscoll J (2006) *Practising Clinical Supervision: a Reflective Approach for Healthcare Professionals*. 3rd edn. Bailliere Tindall, Edinburgh

Francis R (2013) Report of the Mid-Staffordshire Foundation NHS Trust public inquiry. www.midstaffspublicinquiry.com/report (accessed 4 November 2015)

Frost N (2010) Professionalism and social change: the implications of social change for the 'reflective practitioner'. In: Bradbury H, Frost N, Kilminster S, Zukas M, eds. *Beyond Reflective Practice: New Approaches to Professional Lifelong Learning*. Routledge, London: 15–24

Gibbs G (1988) *Learning by Doing: a Guide to Teaching and Learning Methods*. Further Education Unit, Oxford Brookes University, Oxford

Kolb D (1984) *Experiential Learning: Experience as the Source of Learning and Development*. Prentice Hall, New Jersey

Kozier B, Erb G, Berman A, Snyder S, Lake R, Harvey S (2007) *Fundamentals of Nursing: Concepts, Process and Practice*. Pearson, Harlow

Roberts M, Ion R (2014) Big ideas – a critical consideration of systemic moral catastrophe in modern health care systems: a big idea from an Arendtian perspective. *Nurse Education Today* **34:** 673 –5

Schön D (2003) *The Reflective Practitioner: How Professionals Think in Action*. Ashgate Publishing Ltd, Aldershot

CHAPTER 4

Making sense of your role, practice and service users

By the end of this chapter you will be able to:

1. Differentiate your role from your practice
2. Discuss the fundamental aspects of patient and service user care
3. Identify a range of different types of knowledge within the workplace.

Introduction

The focus of this chapter is to enable you to make sense of your role, your practice and patient, client and service user care. For simplicity's sake, the term 'service user' will be used to refer to the care that we offer to the patients, carers and clients whom we serve. We will also explore different sources of knowledge that can be found within the workplace and identify how knowledge generates expertise.

Who am I?

It would be tempting to answer the question 'Who am I?' by reaching for your job description. This would be inappropriate for two reasons. First, practice-based learners are not employees and do not have a job description, whereas work-based learners often realise that their job descriptions, if not out of date at the start of their studies, quickly become out of date as the scope of their practice changes and new skills are developed. We saw in Chapter 2 that work is deeply meaningful because it leads to learning that enables you to become and shapes your sense of self and your 'personhood'. Dave and Sarbjit are learning to become new professionals and by gaining expertise will learn not only to perform their roles but how to be an assistant practitioner and staff nurse. Dall'Alba (2009, p. 44) argues that workplace traditions tend to be taken for granted and are not transparent. Put more simply, a fish is the last to discover water. Becoming a health and social care professional involves a transformation of the self in order for professional routines and traditions to become embodied within us.

One approach that can help us to understand who we are is to 'pull-apart' our role from our practice. In other words, to differentiate between who we are and what we do. Daniel, a work-based learner and one of my students, created a mind map that portrayed aspects of his working role and the responsibilities that he had as a senior support worker (see *Figure 4.1*). Mind mapping is a useful and creative activity developed by Tony Buzan (2002) (Buzan and Buzan, 2003) that enables you to capture your thinking in order to make sense of something or to plan a project. You will see that the left-hand side of Daniel's mind map portrays his role, whereas the right-hand side describes the responsibilities that make up his practice. He has used branches to signify different aspects of his working life and sub-branches to break down topics. Each branch has one word and he has included symbols and pictures to demonstrate aspects of his practice; for example an image of a ball on a painted line to indicate his professional 'boundaries'.

Activity 8

Create a mind map using no more than 50 words, detailing your workplace role, the boundaries of your practice and your responsibilities. Your mind map can be produced using mind mapping software or hand-drawn using colours, symbols or icons.
Your mind map needs to differentiate between:

■ Who you are (your role)
■ What you do (your responsibilities)
■ What you are not permitted to do (the boundaries of your practice).

There are several mind mapping resources available on the internet, including mind mapping software:
iMindMap: http://imindmap.com
FreeMind: http://freemind.sourceforge.net/wiki/index.php/Download

Figure 4.1 Daniel's mind map demonstrating his role and responsibilities

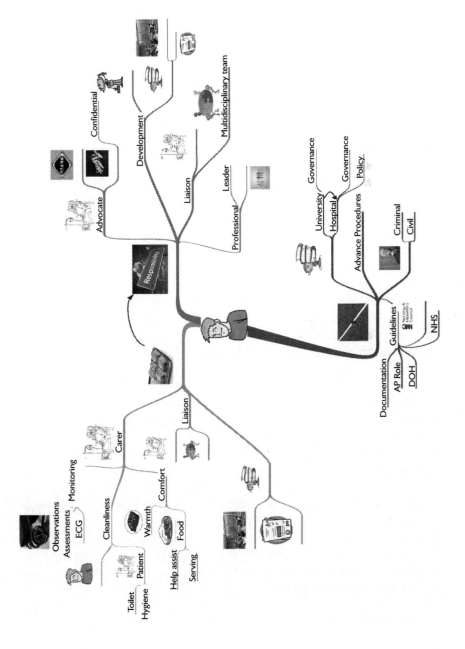

You will recall that Chapter 1 started with the question: 'Why is it that the simplest of questions always seem to be the hardest to answer?' Trying to unpick your role from your responsibilities is challenging! It is important to understand the boundaries of your role because as roles change, role boundaries can become quite fluid. Undertaking an assessment of your competence will sharpen your understanding of the boundaries of your practice as you are required to demonstrate your understanding of safe, effective and efficient practice and provide a rationale for your actions in order demonstrate your underpinning knowledge. Health and social care workers tend to describe their roles in the context of the activities that they engage in. Research by Kessler et al (2012) involving healthcare assistants – by far the largest group of support workers employed by the NHS – demonstrated that participants described their roles based on their clinical tasks and responsibilities. Consequently, the findings from the interviews conducted with the healthcare assistants demonstrated five clusters or 'types' of healthcare assistant:

- Cluster 1 – Bedside technicians: healthcare assistants who provide direct patient-centred care that includes bathing, feeding and bed-making on a daily basis and other routine clinical and technical skills, such as blood glucose monitoring, clinical observations and escorting patients.
- Cluster 2 – Ancillaries: This is a healthcare assistant who undertakes a restricted range of activities, such as bed-making and keeping stores stocked.
- Cluster 3 – Citizen healthcare assistant: The citizen healthcare assistant is a blend of the bedside technician and ancillary healthcare assistant, but works to support a strong team ethos and is as committed to the support of qualified nurses as he or she is to delivering patient care.
- Cluster 4 – All-rounders: This type of healthcare assistant provides direct and indirect patient care, but engages in more advanced clinical skills, such as phlebotomy, performing electrocardiograms (ECGs) and simple dressing changes. All-rounders have a diverse, demanding and wide-ranging role.
- Cluster 5 – Experts: Expert healthcare assistants undertake the same routine technical tasks as the other types of healthcare assistants, but perform complex clinical tasks with greater regularity. They tend to be more highly qualified and on a higher salary.

(Kessler et al, 2012, pp. 125–9)

One of the dangers of viewing yourself in this way, however, is that it can stop you from reflecting on who you are. This can create a barrier to learning, as reflection requires you to learn by noticing yourself.

Another way of understanding your role is to consider how actors get into character. This is achieved through a thorough understanding of how people think and talk and how thoughts and language shape behaviour. For example, the television actor David Suchet not only read all of Agatha Christie's novels in preparation for his role as the Belgian detective Hercule Poirot, but compiled a list of over 90 of his mannerisms and characteristics to faithfully recreate his character (Suchet, 2013). The authenticity of an actor's performance is critical if he or she is to fulfil the role for which he or she is cast. In Chapter 7 we will focus on how you can become an authentic health and social care professional.

What do I do?

We have seen that practice-based and work-based learning is learning that occurs informally, but it is also learning that is *situated* within particular communities of practice. I am sure that your mind map, like Daniel's, featured a whole range of tasks and activities. Generating a list of tasks and activities is useful, but does not really help us understand the relationships that shape activities and how our practice is *situated*. Activity 9 has been designed to help you understand how your practice is situated in relationship to others.

Activity 9 will have enabled you to see how your practice is situated in relation to your colleagues. You may have been surprised at how your practice has changed or is changing as a result of your status as a practice-based or work-based learner. This activity is particularly useful in enabling learners to understand how they work in partnership with their colleagues. Partnership and collaborative working are vital aspects of contemporary health and social care practice as they have a direct effect on the quality of care that service users receive.

Activity 9

Imagine a dartboard:

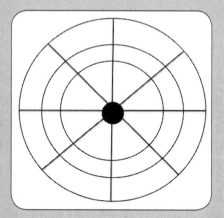

Appendix 1 (p. 123) contains a blank copy of a dartboard that should be used to complete this activity.
Make a copy of it and follow the instructions carefully:

1. Insert your name in the bulls-eye (the very centre of your dartboard).
2. Now make a list of all the colleagues that you work with at least once a week (if you are a work-based learner) or are currently working with (if you are on placement). If you have just started a new placement and you do not know the names of all of your colleagues, complete the exercise based on your last placement.
3. Now insert the names of colleagues in each segment of the dartboard on the basis of how much direct contact you have with them:
   - Insert the initials of your colleagues in each segment.
   - Use different colours to shade each segment based on their professional groupings (e.g. red = nursing, green = occupational therapy, blue = physiotherapy, brown = administrative staff, grey = medical staff, pink = housekeeping staff, yellow = dietetics, white = speech and language therapist, purple = chaplains, mauve = social workers).
   Remember that outer segments will include names of the people that you have least contact with.

Whom do I serve?

Again, it would be rather simplistic to generate a list of different types of service users that you encounter in your clinical and therapeutic practice on a daily basis. In fact this would be inappropriate, as any attempt to pigeon-hole or label service users into 'neat' little boxes would be unprofessional, as our care needs to be client- rather than category-centred. In the last section we touched on the importance of partnership and collaborative working. Activity 10, although similar to Activity 9, will enable you to understand the relationship that exists between colleagues and should feature a service user of your choice.

Activity 10

Use a second blank copy of the image of a dartboard in Appendix 1 (p. 123) to complete this activity. Again, read follow the instructions carefully:

1. Think about a service user that you have cared for recently and write his or her initials in the bulls-eye (the very centre of your dartboard).
2. With your chosen service user in the centre of your diagram, insert the names of your colleagues in the segments of the dartboard on the basis of how much direct contact you think they have with your chosen service user:
   - Insert the initials of your colleagues in each segment.
   - Use different colours to shade each segment based on their professional groupings (e.g. red = nursing, green = occupational therapy, blue = physiotherapy, brown = administrative staff, grey = medical staff, pink = housekeeping staff, yellow = dietetics, white = speech and language therapist, purple = chaplains, mauve = social workers).
   Remember that outer segments will include names of the colleagues that have the least contact with your chosen service user.

Activity 10 will help you to understand the relationships that exist between service users and members of your clinical or therapeutic team. It is likely that you have the most direct contact with your service user, including his or her spouse, partner, family and friends. Often in health and social care settings, the most junior and inexperienced members of health and social care teams have the closest relationships with clients and service users. Hornby and Atkins (2000) describe 'face workers' as workers who are the human face of the helping services; the faces that are 'known' and become the first point of contact for service users. It is important to remember that service users communicate with whoever is the most accessible and whoever they feel the most comfortable with, and may not necessarily take into account the seniority or experience of the 'face worker'.

Knowledge

You will have seen from the vignettes that learning at work arises when we perform a task. This type of learning is known as 'informal'. Informal learning arises from how you perform within your role and draws on your levels of awareness and understanding; your personal development; your ability to make decisions and solve problems; and your ability to work within a team and use your judgement, skills and knowledge. There are several types of knowledge within the workplace, and we will explore knowledge types using Vignette 5.

Vignette 5: Dave learning with his mentor Kate

One morning Dave received a call from Kate, who had received a referral of a new client – Mrs James – who had balance problems having been newly-diagnosed with Parkinson's disease. As promised, Kate asked Dave whether he could score Mrs James using the Berg balance scale. Kate supervised Dave as he began explaining the Berg balance scale to Mrs James. This was achieved by demonstrating the positions that Mrs James would need to be in order for her balance to be assessed. Dave did this by injecting some humour into the situation to alleviate her embarrassment, with Dave referring to one position – where her arms needed to be outstretched to the front, as 'like a bad zombie movie!'. Dave proceeded to score Mrs James's ability to hold her arms out straight as previously instructed by Kate and recalled her technique when assessing another client. Fifteen minutes into the assessment, Dave was concerned that Mrs James was becoming tired and asked Kate whether it was okay to continue with the assessment. At the end of the visit with Mrs James, Dave and Kate compared their Berg balance scores and Kate gave Dave some feedback on his skills in assessing Mrs James.

Vignette 5 demonstrates the different types of knowledge as described by Baumard (1999), which are used in practise. Dave drew on his *abstract knowledge* by referring to zombie movies in a bid to help Mrs James relax and alleviate any embarrassment she may have had in adopting some of the physical positions required in order for her balance to be assessed. Abstract knowledge tends to be knowledge that is general, universal and easy to communicate. The completion of a valid assessment needed to be done in a way that produced findings that are reliable – an accurate, objective and measurable record of Mrs James's balance. This required Dave to draw on his *technical knowledge*. This type of knowledge required Dave to have the capability to accomplish the task set for him by Kate in line with best practice in the assessment of clients using the Berg balance scale. Dave used his *practical knowledge* (sometimes referred to as social wisdom) to enable Mrs James to feel safe while being observed by Kate, his workplace mentor. Practical knowledge comprises soft or people skills (sometimes known as 'affective' skills) and is required to ensure that social interactions are successful. Lastly, Dave drew on what is called *conjectural knowledge*. The word 'conjecture' means when someone gives an opinion based on incomplete information and occurs in situations where there is uncertainty or unpredictability. Dave was worried that he was taking too long to complete Mrs James's assessment, that she was becoming too tired, and that his assessment results may be inaccurate. In order to resolve his concern, quite rightly, he sought advice and reassurance from Kate. It is not necessary for you to remember the different types of knowledge discussed in relation to Vignette 5, but it is important to remember that knowledge has different elements that we draw on, often unknowingly or tacitly, in almost all practical situations with service users. The next section will explore how knowledge becomes known in order for expertise to be developed.

Knowing

One of the most common ways we can characterise how knowledge becomes known is by the level of expertise that a practitioner has developed and which determines his or her level of practise. Expertise is regarded as your ability to demonstrate a combination of knowledge and skills within your particular field. We will explore expertise using Vignette 6.

In Vignette 6 we see how Sarbjit's knowledge and skills were assessed by Pedro within a clinical environment that was familiar to her; namely a nursing home. Mr Fazakerley had two problems that Sarbjit will have been familiar with, given the experience that she had accrued both before and since commencing her nursing degree. Sarbjit had previously worked in a nursing home and was able to demonstrate some knowledge and understanding of the management of urinary incontinence. Pedro, her workplace mentor, had agreed with her suggestions and drew her attention to an additional consideration.

Vignette 6: Sarbjit on placement within a district nursing team

Sarbjit was 3 days into her new placement within a district nursing team based in a large health centre located within a busy urban area. Pedro, her new workplace mentor, had been asked to visit Mr Fazakerley, an 86-year-old gentleman who lived in a nursing home. Mr Fazakerley had recently been discharged from hospital into the care of the nursing home and had a leg ulcer and problems with urinary incontinence, having been catheterised during his hospital stay.

On arrival at the nursing home Pedro and Sarbjit signed the visitors' book and were escorted to Mr Fazakerley's room, which was on the third floor. Sarbjit was impressed by the size and design of the nursing home and, as she accompanied Pedro, thought about the care home that she used to work in before starting her nursing degree. Pedro introduced himself and Sarbjit to Mr Fazakerley and then asked him whether Sarbjit could assess his leg ulcer under supervision. Pedro asked Sarbjit if she would wash her hands, don a pair of gloves and an apron and carefully remove Mr Fazakerley's dressing. He then advised Sarbjit to observe, examine and describe what she could see, both on the dressing that had been removed and the appearance of the wound itself, now that it had been exposed. Pedro demonstrated the use of the Walsall community leg ulcer assessment tool to assess the leg ulcer and re-dressed the ulcer aseptically.

Pedro then asked Mr Fazakerley about his urinary continence problems. Mr Fazakerley explained that he found walking difficult and could not always get to the toilet in time during the day, although he managed to use his urinal bottle at night with the assistance of nursing staff. Pedro undertook an assessment of Mr Fazakerley using the community trust's assessment tool and asked Sarbjit whether she could suggest ways of managing Mr Fazakerley's continence problems.

Sarbjit suggested the use of a urinary sheath during the daytime to alleviate Mr Fazakerley's anxiety and to build his confidence; and the use of a toileting regime to manage his urinary urgency. Sarbjit also suggested that Mr Fazakerley's fluid intake needed to be monitored to ensure that he did not consume too many caffeine-based drinks, which are known to cause bladder instability, urinary frequency and urgency. Pedro agreed with this management plan but also suggested that Mr Fazakerley's urine should be tested to rule out the possibility of a hospital-acquired urinary tract infection.

Later that evening Sarbjit wrote up a reflection piece based on her day spent with Pedro. Sarbjit reflected on the expertise that she was able to draw on with regard to the assessment of a patient with continence problems, but included within her action plan the need to read up on wound assessment skills.

It is useful to consider what is meant by expertise using a well-established model of skill acquisition that has been applied to clinical nursing (Benner, 1984). Dreyfus and Dreyfus (1986) argue that human beings acquire skill through instruction and experience and do not leap from 'knowing that' to 'know-how' as skills require concrete experience in real situations. They identified five stages of skills acquisition:

- *Novice:* A novice learns to recognise facts and features that are relevant to a skill and is aware of the rules that determine his or her actions. Novices may not possess any previous experience of the situation in which they are expected to perform, therefore novices can only judge their performance on how they have abided by the rules.
- *Advanced beginner:* A novice becomes an advanced beginner when he or she has considerable experience of coping with real situations and uses his or her previous experiences to recognise similarities in new situations. His or her performance is marginally acceptable, therefore the previous experience is more important than being able to merely describe features within a new situation.
- *Competence:* A competent performer views a situation as having not only a set, but a constellation of facts. The situation therefore comprises a range of facts that become *greater than the sum of their parts* because they lead to a conclusion being drawn, a decision being made or an expectation being investigated.
- *Proficiency:* Proficient performers become deeply involved in their work, to the extent that some features will be more salient while others can safely recede into the background. Proficient performers work intuitively and can

recognise similarities almost unknowingly through the development of an ability that is used constantly to complete everyday tasks. Proficient performers also know how to modify their response to changing situations.

■ *Expertise:* Experts know what to do because they possess mature and practised understanding. Their skill has become so much a part of them that they are almost unconscious of it. Experts have the ability to focus in on the precise features of a problem without the need to engage in analysis or the consideration of a wide range of alternative solutions.

Activity 11

Read Vignettes 5 and 6 again, featuring Dave assessing Mrs James (with Kate) and Sarbjit working under the supervision of Pedro. Try and identify which level of expertise that Dave and Sarbjit possess and determine why.

Activity 11 will have enabled you to make sense of expertise; where knowledge and understanding creates knowing that can be put into practise. You may have also noticed that to a certain extent Dave's and Sarbjit's levels of expertise differ slightly as their levels of experience are different and their roles require different types of expertise. Sarbjit has experience that she has been able to draw on and contribute to the management of Mr Fazakerley's continence problems, whereas Dave is developing his expertise in the context of a more structured assessment that he needs to be proficient at in order to fulfil a particular role within a particular service that serves a particular type of service user. We can see again how practice-based and work-based learning differ; not only in terms of the purpose of learning, but the direction in which the learning is leading with regard to the development of a proficient adult nurse, capable of being employed in a range of clinical areas (Sarbjit) and a proficient assistant practitioner who will remain within the same therapeutic area, albeit with a narrower range of more specialist skills (Dave).

Summary

This chapter has tried to make sense of the three key elements that characterise learning within the workplace – your role (who you are), your practise (what you do) and your service users (the people you serve). Unpicking your role from your practise is challenging, but can help you learn through an approach to reflection where the focus is moved away from tasks and activities and towards yourself. Your clinical and therapeutic practice, and therefore your learning, is located or *situated* within a community of practice that is formed by a complex web of relationships. The proximity of these relationships to yourself will vary, but the proximity that you have to your service users as a 'face worker' is close. Clinical and therapeutic interventions require several different types of knowledge. The accumulation of experience, knowledge and skills shapes the level of expertise that you hold based on prolonged exposure to a range of workplace situations. Lastly, as we saw with Sarbjit and Dave, the development of expertise is shaped by the particular requirements of the professional role that you are being educated to fulfil and whether that learning is associated with preparation for practice, or education within practice.

Key points

- In order to differentiate between your role and practise you need to ask yourself who you are and what you do, in addition to identifying the boundaries of your responsibilities
- Mind mapping is a useful creative thinking tool that can help you make sense of your role, practice and service users
- Viewing yourself on the basis of the activities and tasks that you complete can stop you from learning, as reflection requires you to learn by noticing yourself
- Working in partnership and collaboration with your colleagues is vital to contemporary health and social care practice, as it has a direct effect on the quality of care that service users receive
- 'Face workers' such as trainees, practice-based and work-based learners, may become the face of an organisation because they have the most direct and constant contact with service users and their families
- Your interactions with service users require abstract, technical, practical and conjectural forms of knowledge and strong social or 'affective' skills
- The acquisition of new skills and knowledge coupled with experience enable you to move from being a novice, experienced beginner and proficient worker towards becoming an expert.

Useful websites

- Royal College of Nursing resources on accountability, delegation and professional issues for healthcare assistants and assistant practitioners: www.rcn.org.uk/development/health_care_support_workers/professional_issues
- Walsall Community Wound/Leg Ulcer Assessment Tools: www.walsallcommunityhealth.nhs.uk/media/91855/enc%2011%20-%20wound%20management%20policy%20final.pdf

References

Baumard P (1999) *Tacit Knowledge in Organizations.* Sage, London

Benner P (1984) *From Novice to Expert: Excellence and Power in Clinical Nursing Practice.* Addison-Wesley Publishing Company, California

Buzan T (2002) *How to Mind Map: the Ultimate Thinking Tool that will Change Your Life.* Thorsons, London

Buzan T, Buzan B (2003) *The Mind Map Book.* BBC Active, London

Dall'Alba G (2009) *Exploring Education Through Phenomenology: Diverse Approaches.* Wiley-Blackwell, Oxford

Dreyfus HL, Dreyfus SE (1986) *Mind Over Machine: the Power of Human Intuition and Expertise in the Age of the Computer.* Basil Blackwell, Oxford

Hornby S, Atkins J (2000) *Collaborative Care: Interprofessional, Interagency and Interpersonal.* 2nd edn. Blackwell, Oxford

Kessler I, Heron P, Dopson S (2012) *The Modernization of the Nursing Workforce: Valuing the Healthcare Assistant.* Oxford University Press, Oxford

Suchet D (2013) *Poirot and Me.* Headline Publishing Group, London

CHAPTER 5

Being a worker and a learner

By the end of this chapter you will be able to:

1. Describe at least two strategies for holding conversations that matter
2. Identify how to negotiate being a worker and a learner
3. Evaluate the most effective way of acting on feedback
4. Analyse a range of strategies to engage in self-negotiated learning.

Introduction

In Chapter 4 we explored three fundamental questions to help you make sense of your role, practice and service users. These were 'Who am I?', 'What do I do?' and 'Whom do I serve?'. You will have seen that it is difficult to pull apart your role from your practise, but that it is important to do so if you are to avoid describing your role purely on the basis of a range of activities. We explored how you can make sense of your position within the multidisciplinary team as a 'face worker' using the two activities featuring the dartboard. Vignettes 5 and 6 featuring Dave and Sarbjit demonstrated the different types of knowledge and levels of expertise that exist within clinical practice environments.

The purpose of this chapter will be to identify some practical approaches that will enable you to capture and exploit the learning opportunities within your practice and working environment. We will consider the use of conversation and how to balance being a worker and a learner, and then explore how feedback can be used. The last section of the chapter will focus on the skills needed to undertake self-negotiated and opportunistic learning.

Having conversations that matter

In order to manage relationships with mentors and other members of the multi-disciplinary team, effective communication skills need to be developed that will ensure that every conversation you have matters. It is beyond the scope of this book to explore communication skills in depth. One approach described by Thomson (2006), however, seeks to differentiate between debate and dialogue in order to 'reframe' your conversation.

Traditionally, debating is understood as a vigorous activity where arguments are associated with winning and losing. Thomson (2006, pp.102–4) argues that in order to hold *conversations that matter*, dialogue is required where the goal is to explore multiple viewpoints that create new possibilities. This requires you to be curious in order to deepen your understanding. This form of inquiry enables you to ask questions that bring to the surface the

Vignette 7: Dave having a conversation with Dominic

After a busy morning, Dave joined Dominic, an occupational therapist, in the staff room for lunch. Dominic asked Dave how life was treating him, to which Dave replied: 'Don't ask!' The rest of the conversation was as follows:

Dominic: 'So, what's troubling you mate?'

Dave: 'Oh, it's Kate, my mentor. I mean she's great to work with, but she never considers my ideas…'

Dominic: 'Okay, give me an example of when she did not consider your ideas.'

Dave then described a recent experience that occurred during a home visit.

Dave: 'I also think she has an attitude problem.'

Dominic: 'Can you describe to me how she has behaved in a way that has annoyed you?'

Dave: 'It was more of a comment really. She suggested that assistant practitioners who take on responsibilities previously undertaken by therapists make some staff feel de-skilled.'

Dominic: 'Perhaps it would be a good idea to mention to Kate that you have been thinking about de-skilling, following that conversation. Why not ask her to share her thoughts on how best to support staff who fear becoming de-skilled?'

assumptions that are held, either from within yourself or by others taking part in the dialogue. It requires that participants suspend their own judgements and are prepared to respect the views of those engaging in dialogue in order to create new understanding and a way forward. Clearly, in order to engage in conversations that matter you need to attend to the content as well as the quality of your communications, as demonstrated in Vignette 7.

Although Dominic is senior to Dave, he did not seek to defend Kate (a fellow therapist) or dismiss Dave's expression of annoyance, but engaged in a dialogue with Dave using questions that enabled him to explore his relationship with Kate in greater depth. Brockbank and McGill (2012) describe two types of conversational structures where spoken phrases are either *surface* or *deep*. Dave's sentences had a surface structure, as he made quite a generalised statement that lacked specific information and suggested that his relationship with Kate had become damaged. Dominic sought to recover some of Dave's superficial statements by using a questioning approach that had a *deep* structure to identify information that Dave had *deleted* from his statement; namely specific experiences and instances of working with Kate and how they were associated with his feelings regarding the value of his ideas and Kate's attitude towards him. Dominic encouraged Dave to explore de-skilling further and to raise the topic at his next meeting with Kate. Dominic's suggestion will not only help Dave to clarify Kate's position on de-skilling, but enable Dave and Kate to reflect together on an important issue.

Vignette 7 illustrates how dialogue can work to ensure that learning can be facilitated between two people using an approach to questioning that moves beyond surface assumptions or shallow perceptions. It also illustrates the importance of maintaining a developmental relationship with your workplace mentor. Raelin (2008, pp. 172–4) argues that developmental relationships in work-based learning are unique as they provide the mentor and mentee with an opportunity for mutual reflection. This can further the self-development of both parties and is particularly powerful when learning is generated from challenges arising from practice.

'Conversations that matter' occur in the most informal of settings, such as at meal times, around a water dispenser or in a staff room, which suggests that these conversations are opportunistic. We will return to the topic of opportunistic learning towards the end of the chapter.

Negotiating being a worker and a learner

We explored the nature of change and the uncertainty that characterises working within health and social care organisations in Chapter 2. Barnett (1999) argues that we live in an age of supercomplexity resulting from major shifts within society that have led to our comprehension of the world being contested and challenged in unpredictable ways. Under these conditions *work has to become learning and learning has to become work*, as being a professional is about being able to handle increasing levels of complexity driven by a range of triggers and drivers, including levels of public spending. Barnett (1999,

Table 5.1 Skills required to balance work and learning (Tennant, 2000)

Skills needed to work and learn	Suggested strategies
The ability to analyse workplace experiences	Analysing experiences that occur at the 'point of care' by engaging in reflection-in-action
The desire to learn from others	Being curious and engaging in conversations that matter
The ability to act without all the facts being available	Recognising the boundaries of your knowledge, skills and competence and engaging in help-seeking
The ability to choose from among multiple courses of action	Consulting with other members of the multidisciplinary team, reading and searching for information
The desire to learn about the organisational culture (e.g. the community, hospital, company or an NHS trust)	Attending team meetings and briefings, reading organisational and corporate news letters, NHS trust/company strategic plan
The ability to use a wide range of resources and activities	Searching an organisation's outward-facing website and the intranet, and identifying expertise, key decision-makers, opinion-formers and clinical experts

p. 42) concludes that work needs to be understood as a place where workers are presented with infinite learning opportunities. Being a worker and a learner is challenging as both roles are closely associated with what it means to be effective in the workplace. Being identified as a learner in the workplace opens up issues related to your position, how you are recognised and how you manage existing relationships with your colleagues. In order to balance work and learning Tennant (2000, pp. 124–7) suggests that learning within the workplace requires the set of skills listed in *Table 5.1*.

These skills will help you to understand the competing and varied interests that shape your work, your clinical group and your professional identity. Use the above list of skills and suggested strategies to assist you in the completion of Activity 12.

Activity 12

You will find a blank copy of a SWOT analysis sheet in Appendix 2 (p. 124), which should be used to complete this activity.

1. Analyse the strengths, weaknesses, opportunities and threats (SWOT) to learning within your current placement or workplace
2. Consider the impact of each aspect on you as a workplace-based or practice-based learner
3. Identify ways that you can minimise the threats to your learning.

The purpose of the last activity was to enable you to identify the barriers to, and the enablers of, learning in addition to the particular features of your current placement or workplace. You will have realised that the list of skills outlined in *Table 5.1* provide some solutions to the challenges of using your workplace for learning. But how do people actually learn? One definition of learning is as follows:

> The combination of processes throughout a lifetime whereby the whole person, body and mind experiences social situations; the content of which is then transformed cognitively, emotively and or practically and integrated into the individual person's biography resulting in a continually changing person.

(Jarvis, 2009, p. 25)

Key learning processes

This definition contains themes that we have already explored. Learning is viewed as being 'lifelong' and is based on experiences and activities that are situated in specific locations. Learning shapes your identity in terms of where you are in the lifecycle and leads to change. In order to break this definition down Jarvis (2009, pp. 26–7) describes six key learning processes:

- *Remembering:* based on the ability to recall previous experiences as your memories are programmed by human interactions
- *Imitating:* acts of 'copying' that arise from your relationships, but that are shaped by tradition and culture
- *Adapting:* where your behaviour or thinking is adjusted in order to fit particular expectations within a situation (or your *life world)*
- *Experimenting:* where you try out a range of possible solutions to identify the one that will 'fit'
- *Reinforcing:* learning associated with, or in response to, a reward
- *Time:* although you have a constant stream of experiences throughout your life, your ability to pursue answers to questions and retain your level of curiosity is based on your personality and consciousness of the effect and impact that time has on your life.

The theory–practice gap

You may have come across a phrase that describes the 'gap' between what you expect to experience as a result of your knowledge and what is actually experienced when you come to put into action knowledge recently acquired or learnt. In clinical settings this is often referred to as the 'theory–practice gap' and is a disjuncture that leads to a separation between your knowledge and what you had hoped to learn from the actual experience. Practice-based and work-based learners such as Sarbjit and Dave may experience the theory–practice gap when returning to their clinical areas following a period of formal learning within university. It can also occur if you have accrued knowledge from previous experiences that is tested in the light of new understanding or when starting a new placement. One approach that can alleviate the theory–practice gap is through guided learning, where you engage in activities such as problem solving in a concerted and effortful way to create interdependence between your knowledge and your engagement in workplace activities (Billett, 2000). In order to demonstrate this we will return to Dave and see what actions he took following his conversation with Dominic.

Vignette 8: Dave in conversation with Kate

Dave arranged to meet up with Kate, his mentor, as he needed her to sign off a module workbook and discuss a reflection piece he wanted to include in his work-based learning portfolio. Towards the end of the meeting Dave decided to ask Kate a question:

Dave: 'You remember the other week at the end of the home visit to Mrs James, when we got talking about assistant practitioner roles?'

Kate: 'Oh yeah, I remember.'

Dave: 'I have been thinking about the de-skilling that you said that might occur if assistant practitioners take on roles that were formerly undertaken by therapists. I was really interested by that observation... and it's really made me think. Can I ask you what might lead a therapist to be worried about being de-skilled by an assistant practitioner?'

Kate: 'That's a very good question and I am glad you have been thinking about de-skilling. It's an issue at present because, as you know, we have two newly-qualified therapists coming into the team. They are new to intermediate care and have not worked with assistant practitioners before. It's difficult for them because although they have skills and knowledge, they need opportunities, like you, to refine their practise. They also need to be given space to build their confidence with a different kind of support to what they would have had as students, so that they can feel part of the team. I guess they need to adapt what they have learnt to ensure they meet the needs of our clients; and as you know Dave, our clients' needs and expectations are quite challenging at times!'

As a result of Dave talking to Kate about the issue of de-skilling, he has learnt that Kate's comments were not aimed directly at him or associated with his role as a trainee assistant practitioner, but linked to the needs of two newly-appointed colleagues and their workplace learning and development as new-starters. Vignette 8 illustrates how theory–practice gaps can naturally occur when there is a disjuncture within the workplace when what you expect to experience, as a result of your knowledge is different to what is actually experienced. Dave has learnt that his new colleagues will need the freedom to practise and refine their knowledge and skills, but that this is a time when a disjuncture may occur between their previous experiences and how they should apply their skills when working in the intermediate care team. Billett (2001) argues that the way workplaces afford opportunities for learning and how individuals elect to engage in activities is central to how we understand workplaces as learning environments. Dave has used his meeting with Kate not only to meet his own learning needs and clarify a viewpoint that he initially found to be challenging, but to understand the learning and development needs of others and how learning opportunities or affordances need to be shared within the intermediate care team. Participation in learning activities is not afforded in similar ways to all individuals within the workplace. Dave has learnt that Kate will be seeking to support his new colleagues in a different way to how she has supported him. Dave has also realised that being a mentor requires careful preparation. He has learnt that although the intermediate care team enables learning and development to occur, the opportunities available will determine the quality of learning that transpires (Billett, 2001).

Negotiating being a worker and a learner is challenging, particularly when the workplace is being used by other learners including newly-qualified healthcare professionals who have particular development needs, as we saw in Vignette 8. In addition to effective mentoring, students find workplace learning satisfying when they receive support from their colleagues, are provided with protected study time, have supportive managers, and, as we saw in the discussion between Dave and Dominic, when they experience positive staff attitudes (Lloyd et al, 2014; Wareing et al, 2014).

Learning and teaching techniques

In the last section we saw how participation within workplace learning requires you to be engaged in work while being intent on identifying and shaping activities to ensure that your knowledge and understanding are being constantly developed to the point where learning almost becomes the central purpose of working. In order for work to be organised to enable learning to occur, workplace mentors, assessors and instructors will use a range of teaching tactics. These include (Bailey and Hughes, 2004):

- Teaching and demonstrating, e.g. explaining the anatomy and physiology of a body system, a disease process or providing instruction on a piece of equipment or use of an assessment tool
- Enabling you to do a 'dry run', e.g. undertaking simulated learning by practising clinical skills using a manikin or practising undertaking the admission of a patient on a friend or colleague
- Providing a question and answer session, e.g. telling a story and setting a scenario to enable you to demonstrate how you might care for an imaginary patient or deal with a notional situation.

The use of all of these tactics requires you to receive verbal or written feedback in response to your actions in order to improve your performance.

Receiving, using and acting on feedback

Practice-based assessments using competencies often require your workplace mentor or assessor to assess your effectiveness, efficiency and the safety of your practice. They also require you to demonstrate sound knowledge. Whether you are being assessed formatively, which is a practice assessment that provides you with a 'dry run', or summatively, where you are observed in practice (in 'real time'), you will receive feedback from your mentor or assessor to enable you recover when you have failed a competency (or been referred in practice) or simply to enhance your performance.

Activity 13

Think about the last time you received feedback, either from a workplace mentor or following a piece of work such as an essay or assignment that you completed:

1. How was the feedback communicated to you?
2. How did you respond to the feedback?
3. What did you do as a result of the feedback?

In order to make sense of how feedback is provided to learners, we will return to Sarbjit who is being assessed by Jasmine during her latest placement.

Vignette 9: Sarbjit's placement on the medical assessment unit

Sarbjit is halfway through her placement on the medical assessment unit in a large inner city NHS hospital trust. She has found the medical assessment unit a difficult and challenging clinical environment as patients are admitted from the accident and emergency department as well directly from their GP with multiple long-term conditions as well as acute illnesses. Sarbjit has arranged to do a formative assessment with Jasmine, her workplace mentor. This practice-based assessment contains a number of competencies associated with being able to undertake, complete and record patient observations that include temperature, pulse, respiration rate and oxygen saturations and use the SBAR (situation, background, assessment, recommendation) tool when summoning medical assistance for a patient whose condition has changed or worsened.

Jasmine suggests that Sarbjit work alongside her during an early shift so that she can participate in the care of a group of patients under supervision and practice the taking of patient observations. Jasmine observes Sarbjit's engagement with a range of patients and relatives and checks her ability to undertake, complete and record patient observations, which she does safely, effectively and efficiently.

Throughout the morning Jasmine asks Sarbjit to explain the significance of the observations that she has recorded and what actions she thinks should be taken. For example, Mr Jones, who was admitted 2 days ago with an exacerbation of his chronic obstructive pulmonary disease, has slight pyrexia, a rapid pulse and increased respirations in comparison to a set of observations undertaken earlier that were within the normal range. Jasmine asks Sarbjit whether she can see any changes in Mr Jones's observations and what actions need to be taken. Sarbjit becomes a little flustered by this question and although she correctly identifies that Mr Jones's temperature has risen, she fails to notice that his respiration rate has increased. Jasmine asks Sarbjit to look at Mr Jones, observe his breathing and describe anything else she feels is significant. Sarbjit notices that Mr Jones is breathing more rapidly, but does not comment on his wheezing, coughing and use of tissues when removing mucus from his mouth.

Jasmine then approaches Mr Jones and demonstrates to Sarbjit how best to reposition him to enable him to breathe more easily. Jasmine also adjusts his oxygen mask. She hands him a sputum pot so that he can expectorate and collect any secretions from his chest. Jasmine explains that it is important to collect, observe and record the volume, colour and consistency of sputum. She then asks Sarbjit what actions need to be taken with regard to Mr Jones's observations. Sarbjit suggests that they should be recorded half an hour later. Jasmine asks Sarbjit what her actions would be if the observations were the same, and she replies that she would report it to the ward sister.

At the end of the shift, Jasmine and Sarbjit sit down in the staff room (which is empty) and discuss the formative assessment that has been undertaken. Jasmine starts by asking Sarbjit to describe the patients that she has looked after and to give some feedback on her own performance in relation to recording observations. She also asks Sarbjit to explain what she has learnt about SBAR with regard to these patients. Sarbjit explains that she felt confident in recording patient observations, but fails to discuss SBAR with regard to any of her patients, including Mr Jones.

Jasmine starts her verbal feedback by recounting examples of good care that she has observed in relation to how Sarbjit engaged with her patients and how she demonstrated a caring and compassionate attitude. She also complemented her on her communication skills and commented on particular communication strategies, such as describing the probe attached to the oxygen saturation machine as 'like a clothes peg'. Jasmine commented that this was a useful analogy that she felt patients would understand. Jasmine then talked Sarbjit through the observations that she had recorded on Mr Jones and pointed out that they had been different from what had been recorded earlier. She then explained that there were a number of obvious and observable changes in Mr Jones's condition, such as the pattern and characteristics of his breathing and the colour and consistency of his sputum, that were significant and needed to be reported. At this point, Sarbjit realised that Mr Jones's condition had changed and suggested to Jasmine that she should have reported these changes to the on-call medical team using the SBAR tool. Jasmine then asked Sarbjit to demonstrate to her how she would have used the SBAR tool based on her assessment of Mr Jones and the observations that had been recorded. Sarbjit was able to describe the situation, her assessment and recommendations, but was a little vague on the background details associated with Mr Jones with regard to the presenting condition that led to his admission to the ward.

Jasmine completed the written feedback form that Sarbjit had brought with her to undertake her assessment and suggested that Sarbjit read up on the care of breathless patients, the signs and symptoms of chest infection and the use of the SBAR tool in preparation for her next formative assessment in 2 weeks' time.

Vignette 9 demonstrates how engagement and participation in learning can take place in a busy clinical environment between a learner and his or her workplace mentor. In the example, Sarbjit has been given an opportunity to demonstrate clinical skills that she will have been taught and assessed on at university; namely the ability to undertake a patient's temperature, pulse, respiration rate and blood pressure. Although she is competent and can recognise when an observation deviates from what is considered to be normal (e.g. a high temperature or a rapid pulse), she is unable to recognise the significance of the observations that she has recorded in the context of the pattern of observations that have already been recorded on Mr Jones and his changing clinical condition. This has been an incident rich in learning for Sarbjit, as Jasmine has provided her with an experience that has extended her learning beyond the boundaries of her existing level of knowledge (Spouse, 1998). Jasmine has demonstrated a strong ability to engage Sarbjit in learning through participation in clinical practice.

Activity 14

Read Vignette 9 again. Make notes on how Jasmine has given feedback to Sarbjit in respect of:

1. The time, place and location
2. The strategies used by Jasmine to involve Sarbjit
3. The outcome of the assessment.

In order to give Sarbjit effective feedback, Jasmine has secured an appropriate time and place to provide verbal and written feedback in an effective manner. Jasmine commences her feedback by asking Sarbjit to describe the assessment that she has undertaken, including the range of patients and activities that she has completed while being assessed by Jasmine. This is a particularly effective way of giving feedback as it starts with Sarbjit, rather than Jasmine, and places her at the centre of the feedback process. Jasmine then uses some probing questions to see what Sarbjit has learnt from the experience and identifies that she fails to mention the SBAR tool. Sarbjit is then given an opportunity to provide some feedback to Jasmine on her own performance before Jasmine provides verbal feedback to Sarbjit that starts with a positive recognition of her skills in giving caring and compassionate treatment, before identifying areas she needs to develop; namely her ability to recognise the significance of patient observations, changes in a patient's condition and the need to report observations using the SBAR tool.

Although Jasmine provides Sarbjit with feedback, it is important that Sarbjit's and Jasmine's feedback is brought together to formulate an action plan that is based on both of their observations. The action plan that is formulated requires Sarbjit to address her development needs with regard to best practice in the nursing care of breathless patients and the use of the SBAR tool. Jasmine then offers Sarbjit another formative assessment that is scheduled to occur 2 weeks later. This will provide Sarbjit with plenty of time to fulfil the action plan that has been negotiated. More importantly, Sarbjit's feedback has been linked to her next formative assessment and therefore the feedback has become 'future-referenced' (Boud and Molloy, 2012). Although Sarbjit's experience of completing her formative assessment was mixed as she became flustered when questioned by Jasmine, she has been provided with feedback that recognises her communication skills and her ability to act in a caring and compassionate manner, and an action plan that anticipates her ability to address her learning needs in time for a further assessment.

In order to receive, use and act on the feedback that you receive from your workplace mentor or assessor it is important to remember that feedback should be understood in the context of your performance rather than your personality and the actions that you have demonstrated rather than your personal characteristics. Boud and Molloy (2012, p. 24) argue that effective feedback should:

- Enable you to link your performance to standards of work, e.g. policies and clinical guidelines, relevant legislation and principles of 'best practice'
- Be a tool to be used for a clear purpose: to enable you to be a safe, effective and efficient healthcare professional who can demonstrate sound knowledge
- Give you an opportunity to judge your own work: to reflect on your own role, practice and patient, client and service user care; and reflect on your professional values
- Compare your judgement with your workplace mentor or assessor's feedback: to play an active rather than passive role in the discussion of your performance
- Enable you to negotiate an action plan: combine the judgement that you have come to and the judgement that your mentor or assessor has made to generate an action plan for improved work.

In some practice-based assessments it may be appropriate for you to seek feedback from clients and service users, particularly in situations where you are being assessed on the use of a particular therapy or where you have undertaken an assessment of a patient. If a patient, client or service user is happy to provide you with feedback, verbal consent must be obtained from your workplace mentor or assessor before it is recorded in your feedback documentation.

Engaging in self-negotiated and autonomous learning

If you are undertaking a work-based learning award such as a Foundation degree or a BSc (Hons) programme in public health or health and social care, you may be given the opportunity to undertake a self-negotiated, independent or autonomous learning module or block of study. These 'shell modules', where you are required to choose a topic of study under the direction of a supervisor or module facilitator, are extremely popular with students and are regarded as a form of 'gold-plated' work-based learning. In order to identify an area of practice that is of personal interest to you it is important that you work in partnership with your employer and the university, who are equal stakeholders (see *Figure 5.1*). Your line manager will need to ensure that your topic is relevant to your role, the development of your practice and the needs of your patients, clients and service users. The university facilitator will need to ensure that your chosen topic of interest meets the learning outcomes and can be assessed fairly and appropriately (Alsop, 2013, p.75).

Figure 5.1 Working in partnership with stakeholders

Negotiating skills

In order to get the most from self-negotiated learning you will need to nego-tiate with a range of people in your organisation to meet the learning objec-tives that form the focus of your studies. Cottrell (2003) describes three aspects of negotiation:

- Stakes: What is at stake? What is your ultimate aim?
- Outcome: What is the ideal outcome for you and your workplace?
- Bottom line: What is the minimum you are willing to accept?

When you are negotiating activities, meetings, observations and clinical visits it is important that you are clear on what you want from a learning experience. In order to succeed in your negotiation with colleagues, it is worth anticipating what your negotiations may lead to so that you can 'bar-gain' in an informed way to secure the most desirable outcome (Cottrell, 2003). The process of negotiation requires you to:

- Identify what would be your ideal solution
- Recognise what would be a good or acceptable outcome for you
- Consider the next best option for you
- Anticipate the most likely option
- Identify the most likely outcome
- Determine what might be the minimum that you think someone is likely to offer you.

In order to negotiate skilfully you will need to:

- Know when to *concede* in terms of deadlines (for the completion of the module or project)
- Identify your *costs* (time, travel)
- Minimise any *risks* (in relation to other demands and fulfilling other responsibilities)
- Manage any *competition* (from other students or learners within the workplace).

Having an awareness of the history of your department or the organisation where you will be completing your negotiated learning will also help you to negotiate in an informed and strategic manner.

Activity 15

Think about a topic or subject of interest that you would like to study. In Appendix 3 (p. 125) you will find a blank PESTLE analysis sheet. Pestle stands for: Political (P), Economic (E), Social (S), Technological (T), Legal (L) and Ethical (E). This tool provides you with specific domains in which to analyse your chosen area of study. Completing a PESTLE analysis will also help you determine what the implications might be of your studies with regard to any changes to practice or innovation that may result from your self-negotiated learning.

In order to identify, negotiate, plan and evaluate your progress you may wish to use a learning agreement or contract. Do not be too put off by the word 'contract', as this is a tool that should be used as an 'agreement' rather than something that is legally binding (Gibbs, 2009). Remember that your learning agreement need not be 'set in stone', as it may be difficult to predict the kind of support you require. A good learning agreement or contract, however, should be a point of reference that makes the promises of all parties, as well as expectations, explicit.

Activity 16

In Appendix 4 (p. 126) you will find a blank learning agreement template. You will see that your agreement has been designed as a week-by-week plan.

1. Identify at least three learning needs for each week of your negotiated study
2. Try and identify people, departments and organisations that you could contact to arrange a meeting with, or even a visit.

Opportunistic learning

The vignettes featuring Dave and Sarbjit show how learning occurs as a result of the creation of opportunities. This requires forward planning in order to identify particular opportunities through which to engage in guided learning with the assistance of your workplace mentor. As we saw in Vignette 9 with Sarbjit, however, workplace mentors are not always available and the nature of self-negotiated study requires you to seek out and secure learning opportunities for yourself.

Figure 5.2 depicts the three core elements of opportunistic learning. The first of element of opportunistic learning is to ask yourself what is at stake. This has already been discussed in relation to the need for negotiation skills that require you to identify your learning aims, the most desirable outcome, and your 'bottom line' or the minimum you are willing to accept when engaging in learning. What's at stake questions may include the availability of your mentor; the level of support that is available to you from within the workplace; and the challenge of balancing your learning goals with other commitments, such as meeting the requirements of your existing workplace role, other study and family commitments. What's at stake questions require you to balance the costs and benefits of engaging in a particular learning project or activity.

The second element of opportunistic learning requires you to identify what learning resources are available to you. These may include clinical experts and colleagues who may be willing to provide coaching or consultation; lay people and expert patients; or people from outside the organisation, such as those employed in the private, voluntary or independent sectors. Identifying the availability of learning opportunities and resources (also called affordances)

Figure 5.2 The opportunistic learning triangle

can be challenging. One approach is to take a step back from your workplace and seek to analyse the environment and identify what the workplace affords you by completing either a SWOT or a PESTLE analysis.

The last element of opportunistic learning is dependent on your level of participation, engagement, motivation, curiosity and creativity, as 'what you make' is dependent on your ability to realise and complete learning opportunities. The use of a learning agreement is a particularly useful strategy for capturing and demonstrating evidence of your learning and may be required as evidence that you have successfully completed your module or project.

Summary

Being a worker and a learner is challenging and requires the development of a range of skills that include knowing when to hold conversations that matter, by using dialogue and attending to the content of communication to ensure that discussion goes beyond surface assumptions. Using conversation is an important strategy that will enable you to engage in opportunistic learning and is an example of how work must become learning and learning must become work. Being a worker and a learner requires you to understand how the workplace is used by other workers for learning, and how their development needs and can be met and how they differ from your own. Workplace mentors and assessors will use a variety of learning and teaching strategies to facilitate your learning and require you to understand how to receive, make sense of and use feedback in an effective and developmental manner. Engaging in self-negotiated or autonomous learning is an opportunity for you to hold equal status as a stakeholder, alongside your university and your employer.

Key points

- Differentiating between debate and dialogue is the key to holding conversations that matter
- Working and learning has become integrated because of the rise of change, uncertainty and supercomplexity within the workplace

- Holding conversations that matter is vital if learning opportunities are to be taken and discussion is to lead to a form of inquiry that enables assumptions to be uncovered and new understanding to be created
- There are several key learning processes that will enable you to balance being a worker and a learner; these include remembering, imitating, adapting, experimenting and reinforcing
- Although you have a constant stream of experiences throughout your life, your ability to pursue answers to questions and retain your level of curiosity is based on your personality and the effect and impact of time
- The 'gap' or disjuncture between what you expect to experience, as a result of your knowledge, and what is actually experienced when you come to put your knowledge into action is called the theory–practice gap
- Guided learning is a useful strategy that can minimise the impact of theory–practice gaps by creating interdependence between your knowledge and your engagement in workplace learning activities
- Engaging in self-negotiated learning requires you to identify what's at stake, what your ultimate aims are, what the ideal outcome is for you and your workplace, and the minimum you are willing to accept.

Useful websites

- PESTLE analysis: http://pestleanalysis.com/pest-analysis/
- SWOT analysis: www.businessballs.com/swotanalysisfreetemplate.htm
- World of Work Based Learning 1: www.youtube.com/watch?v=mzYkZJG2fQo
- World of Work Based Learning 2: www.youtube.com/watch?v=2hrDtfpIRo8

References

Alsop A (2013) *Continuing Professional Development in Health and Social Care: Strategies for Lifelong Learning.* 2nd edn. Wiley-Blackwell, Oxford

Bailey TR, Hughes KL (2004) *Working Knowledge: Work-based Learning and Education Reform.* Routledge, London

Barnett R (1999) Learning to work and working to learn. In: Boud D, Garrick J, eds. *Understanding Learning at Work.* Routledge, London: 29–44

Billett S (2000) Guided learning at work. *Journal of Workplace Learning* **12**(7): 272–85

Billett S (2001) Learning through work: workplace affordances and individual engagement. *Journal of Workplace Learning* **13**(5): 209–14

Boud D, Molloy E (2012) *Feedback in Higher and Professional Education: Understanding it and Doing it Well.* Routledge, London

Brockbank A, McGill I (2012) *Facilitating Reflective Learning: Coaching, Mentoring and Supervision.* 2nd edn. Kogan Page, London

Cottrell S (2003) *Skills for Success: the Personal Development Planning Handbook.* Palgrave, Basingstoke

Gibbs P (2009) Learning agreements and work-based higher education. *Research in Post-Compulsory Education* **14**(1): 31–41

Jarvis P (2009) *Learning to be a Person in Society.* Routledge, London

Lloyd B, Pfeiffer D, Dominish J et al (2014) The New South Wales Allied Health Workplace Study: barriers and enablers to learning in the workplace. *BMC Health Services Research* **14**: 134

Raelin JA (2008) *Work-Based Learning: Bridging Knowledge and Action in the Workplace.* Jossey-Bass, San Francisco

Spouse J (1998) Scaffolding student learning in clinical practice. *Nurse Educ Today* **18**(4): 259–66

Tennant M (2000) Learning to work, working to learn: theories of situational education. In: Symes C, McIntyre J, eds. *Working Knowledge: the New Vocationalism and Higher Education.* SRHE/Open University Press, Buckingham

Thomson B (2006) *Growing People: Learning and Developing from Day to Day Experience.* Chandos, Oxford

Wareing M, Chadwick K, Baggs H (2014) Student satisfaction with work-based learning: evaluation of a Foundation Degree Health & Social Care programme. *International Journal of Practice-based Learning in Health and Social Care* **2**(2): 65–79

CHAPTER 6

Using your workplace for learning

By the end of this chapter you will be able to:

1. Analyse how workplaces can be used for learning
2. Explain the difference between practice and practise
3. Discuss the challenges and opportunities of workplace learning.

Introduction

In this chapter you will explore how learning occurs in the workplace, the different dimensions of clinical and therapeutic practice, how activities can stimulate learning, and the importance of practice-based assessments undertaken with workplace mentors and assessors.

How workplaces are used for learning

When we talk about work-based or practice-based learning, the assumption is that working and learning occur simultaneously. Boud and Solomon (2001) describe this feature of work-based learning as coincident, in that the tasks we complete are influenced by the nature of work while work is influenced by the nature of learning that occurs, so that the two are complementary. This means that workers have to balance the needs of both roles, as workers and learners. This presents work-based learners with a challenge, as working requires us to provide a service while learning is concerned with acquiring knowledge.

In Chapter 1 we discussed the importance of reflection in order to help you learn by noticing what is happening around you and by looking *within* yourself to identify what you are thinking and feeling. However, reflection is also important if you are to understand not only what you have learnt, but how you have learnt. Reflection is critical because it enables learning that leads you to know not only that you have identified a problem, but also how you have solved a problem. The type of learning undertaken in work-based and practice-based settings is referred to as 'informal' in order to distinguish it from learning undertaken formally within a classroom or as a result of a lecture. Informal learning gives you greater freedom and flexibility, although it does require greater commitment and motivation from you to attend to activities and opportunities at a personal level (Eraut, 2004). Like reflection, informal learning is personal because it requires you to use your memories and experiences; to take notes, ask and observe; to recognise learning opportunities; and to act in a deliberative way by discussing and reviewing your actions and planning future learning activities. In order to make sense of what is learnt within the workplace, we return to Dave in Vignette 10.

Vignette 10: Dave learning with Kate, his mentor, through patient assessment

Following his first formative assessment, Dave arranged with a second formative assessment with his mentor Kate, which was scheduled 1 month before his final summative practice-based assessment was due. As two new clients had been referred to the intermediate care team, Kate and Dave agreed to spend a morning working together so that Dave could observe Kate completing patient assessments and assist in the creation of rehabilitation intervention plans.

Mr Shah had recently been discharged from the local stroke unit and had been referred to the intermediate care team for ongoing rehabilitation to improve his mobility and balance. Kate undertook an assessment of Mr Shah's balance using the Berg balance scale. Dave provided Mr Shah with reassurance while Kate asked him to lift his limbs in order to assess his balance. At the end of the assessment, Kate asked Dave to complete a Berg balance scale sheet on Mr Shah.

At the end of the morning, Kate and Dave reviewed their score sheets and Dave was asked to explain to Kate what mobility and movement needs he thought Mr Shah had on the basis of his assessment. Kate then asked Dave to make some notes on how the visit to Mr Shah had gone while Kate documented the care she had given. Kate and Dave then wrote the mobility section of Mr Shah's rehabilitation intervention care plan.

Dave thanked Kate for enabling him to work with Mr Shah and asked whether he could undertake the next Berg balance scale assessment under Kate's supervision. Kate agreed to inform Dave when she had received a referral of the next new client with balance problems. Kate also suggested that Dave write a piece of reflection based on his experiences of observing and assessing clients using the Berg balance scale and that he research the use of balance assessments in stroke patients for the prevention and management of falls.

Vignette 10 is a good example of how working and learning coincide, and how learners have to be supported to fulfil their role while using new experiences for learning. Kate ensured that Dave participated in her assessment of Mr Shah and had an opportunity to capture his observations and new knowledge at a time appropriate for them all. Undertaking a Berg balance scale assessment was a particularly useful learning opportunity for Dave as he was required to interact with Mr Shah; to observe Kate; to undertake his own patient assessment, justify his findings, and identify the needs of Mr Shah; and suggest possible solutions to the problems identified. The experience also afforded Dave the opportunity to reflect on his learning experience and link his new knowledge to other aspects of practice; namely the use of Berg balance scoring in the management and prevention of falls in at-risk clients. Finally, Kate realised that Dave needed additional experience and agreed to inform Dave of further learning opportunities with clients with balance problems.

Eraut (2004) identified eight particular areas that demonstrate what can be learned in the workplace: task performance; role performance; awareness and understanding; academic knowledge and skills; personal development; decision-making and problem solving; team work and judgement. *Table 6.1* suggests how Dave learnt from his experience with Kate and Mr Shah using the eight areas described by Eraut.

We have seen that informal learning occurs through social interactions as we work alongside colleagues and clients. This suggests successful informal learning is dependent on the quality of human relationships. Research undertaken into the factors that influence informal learning suggests that having colleagues who possess an interest in their field of practise and can demonstrate their professional capability creates a culture in which informal learning prospers, particularly when learners participate in a range of activities and interactions that build their knowledge (Billett, 2001; Berg and Chyung, 2008).

Table 6.1 The eight areas demonstrating what can be learned in the workplace (Eraut, 2004) using the example of Vignette 10

Area	Example
1. Task performance *For example speed, complexity, skills required, communication, collaboration*	*Dave has observed the completion of a Berg balance scale assessment, which requires good communication skills as patients are asked to stand and flex their limbs*
2. Role performance *For example prioritisation, range of responsibility, coping with the unexpected*	*Assessing a new client in his or her home takes time and visiting a client in his or her own home for the first time may lead to unexpected experiences. Mr Shah needed the reassurance of Dave and Kate to feel safe while having his balance assessed*
3. Awareness and understanding *For example other people and colleagues, problems, risks, contexts, values*	*Dave has learnt that he needs to understand how Kate undertakes an assessment with a client using her own approach to manage any hazards and minimise risks*
4. Academic knowledge and skills *For example use of evidence, research, knowing what you might need to know, resources, learning how to use and apply theory*	*Dave has been encouraged by Kate to engage in further reading to make sense of how patients' Berg balance scores link to the management and prevention of falls*

What is the difference between practice and practise?

In Chapter 1 we made the distinction between the word 'practice', which means the carrying out, or the *exercise of a profession*, and the word 'practise', which means to *exercise the skills of one's trade or profession* or to *exercise one's professional skill*. The word 'practice' is a noun, a word used as the name

Table 6.1 The eight areas demonstrating what can be learned in the workplace (Eraut, 2004) using the example of Vignette 10 (continued)

5. Personal development For example self-evaluation, handling emotions, building relationships, consulting with others, accessing expertise, learning from experience	*Dave has had to assess his own ability to interact with Mr Shah and Kate*
6. Decision making and problem solving For example dealing with complexity, team decision making, problem analysis, managing a process within a timescale	*Dave has learnt that the use of an assessment tool, such as the Berg balance scale, is critical in identifying the needs of clients and therefore creating a rehabilitation intervention plan*
7. Teamwork For example collaboration, joint planning, problem solving, mutual learning	*Dave has had to build a good working relationship with Kate to enable him to know when to ask questions and to start to assist in the creation of Mr Shah's rehabilitation intervention plan*
8. Judgement For example quality of performance, outcomes, priorities, values, levels of risk	*Dave has had an excellent opportunity to observe Kate, a physiotherapist, engaging with a client and to assess the quality of her performance and identify best practice in dealing with clients with mobility and balance problems*

of a person, place or thing, or a describing word; whereas the word 'practise' is a verb (a word indicating an action, state or occurrence), a *doing* word.

Wenger (1998) argues that practice is not just about doing something 'in and of itself' but doing something in a historical or social context that has structure and meaning and includes activities that are hidden as well as obvious. When you engage in practice you have to understand the relationship between your actions and their meaning, as your actions correspond to conventions regarding what is considered 'best practice' in health and social care settings. Some knowledge gained in practice settings is explicit and generated from the language, tools, documents and procedures that are governed by regulations and procedures. Other knowledge is hidden or tacit and gained from subtle clues, underlying assumptions and rules of thumb (Wenger, 1998). This second form of knowledge, called hidden or tacit knowledge, is difficult and sometimes almost impossible to put into words, which is another reason why reflection is such an important tool for learning from practice. Jarvis (2009) argues that because learning occurs in specific situations throughout our lives it is important to recognise our perception of the situation, as it will affect our understanding of the event and help prevent us taking our initial perceptions of it for granted. The relationship between your personal commitment and activity (your personal 'agency') and how your learning drives your intentions and activities are closely related to how you 'gaze at' or view the world (Billett, 2008).

Learning through activity

We have seen that professional practice is a social activity, but when we use the word practise we are referring to the nature of the skilled activities that occur within a profession or a professional community. Engeström (2005) argues that learning occurs when you engage in a range of activities within the workplace because:

- You learn from achieving your goals, which maybe personal to you or goals that need to be achieved by your team
- Learning occurs within settings where different viewpoints and opinions are voiced and different interests are expressed, as activities are shaped by different practice traditions

- Learning is shaped by history and activities are shaped over time; the history that shapes learning may be local or arise from the shared experiences of an organisation
- Learning arises from tension, where there may be a contradiction that leads to conflict and disturbances
- Learning from long cycles of activity can be transformative, as change starts to occur as a result of collaboration and collective action.

Activity 17

Think about a particularly vivid client, patient or service user that you have come into contact with recently and the activities that you engaged in while caring for him or her. Identify:

1. Your personal goals when caring for that person
2. The different viewpoints and opinions that shaped his or her care
3. The historical influences from within the organisation that influenced the care that was given
4. Whether any tension, conflict or disturbances shaped the care that was given
5. The impact collaboration within your team had on the care that was given.

We will explore how these five dimensions of activity lead to learning using Vignette 11.

Vignette 11 demonstrated how a personal learning goal and the goals within a team of workers create learning activities as Sarbjit's learning objective was to attend the ward team meeting, which in turn needed to be held to ensure that the ward's nursing staff could meet their goals as a team. The ward team meeting was structured using a chair person (Sarah, the ward manager) who used an agenda of items and minutes to ensure that action points from the previous meeting were not only recorded but that evidence could be gathered to demonstrate actions had been taken; in this case by the senior staff nurse and ward clerk. The minutes form a historical record that not only record actions associated with the ward's nursing team but activity associated with the wider organisation, as illustrated by the contribution made by the healthcare assistant in her role as a protected mealtime champion.

Indira raised the issue of patient consent following the introduction of bedside handovers. This led to some discussion and debate. Sarbjit observed her nursing colleagues engaging in an activity that enabled them to collaborate to

Vignette 11: Sarbjit attends a ward team meeting

Sarbjit was coming to the end of her placement and asked her mentor Mandy whether she could attend the ward team meeting. Mandy discussed this with the ward manager, Sarah, who agreed and Sarbjit joined the rest of the nursing staff in the day room for the ward team meeting held on a Thursday afternoon. Sarbjit sat next to Mandy and was given an agenda and minutes of the last meeting.

Sarah opened the meeting and thanked people for attending and then asked everyone to introduce themselves. Sarah then went through the minutes of the last meeting to check for accuracy. She reviewed the 'matters arising' or action points that it had been agreed needed to be addressed at the last meeting. Sarah explained what she had done in relation to the action points that she was responsible for, and the senior staff nurse and ward clerk also outlined what actions they had taken based on what had been discussed and agreed.

Sarbjit listened to the discussions that followed based on items on the meeting agenda, which included the new dignity policy, a new procedure for requesting study leave and an update from one of the healthcare assistants who is a protected mealtime champion. One of the items on the agenda related to the bedside handover of patients that had been introduced on the ward 8 weeks earlier. Sarbjit listened to this discussion with interest. This new approach to the handover had been introduced during the first week of her placement and required staff to have a collective patient handover meeting in the office, followed by a bedside handover that was given within the two teams of nurses responsible for their own patients. Indira, the leader of the green team, raised the issue of patient consent and suggested that each patient should be asked whether he or she was happy for nurses to carry out a bedside handover. This sparked some debate and discussion regarding what would happen if a patient refused. Eventually, it was agreed that should a patient refuse to give consent to a bedside handover, he or she could be taken into the office where the nursing staff could involve him or her in a handover. It was also agreed that the ward information leaflet for patients needed to be updated to reflect this change in practice. This was recorded in the minutes of the meeting as an action point and the meeting concluded. Sarbjit found the meeting particularly interesting as she had learnt how a formal meeting worked and why an agenda and minutes were necessary.

find a novel solution to the problem of patient privacy and consent that might be compromised when bedside handovers are introduced and other patients and relatives may hear what is being discussed. Indira and the other members of the nursing team all had an understanding of informed consent, and there are guidelines produced by the Department of Health and trust policies that all members of nursing staff are required to uphold in daily practise. However, government and hospital policies cannot cover every eventuality. Vignette 11 demonstrates that sometimes actions need to be taken that lead to a practice that is particular to a workplace, or a particular clinical area. As a result, practitioners develop wisdom that cannot be found in any textbook. In Vignette 11, Sarbjit's colleagues had to adapt their knowledge to ensure that their practise remained knowingly skilful to meet a range of different circumstances, which led to the generation of a particular form of new knowledge about bedside handovers.

Sarbjit's engagement in this activity and her attendance of the ward team meeting has been a rich learning opportunity. When she asked her mentor whether she could attend, she learnt that it might not have been possible if there was a particularly sensitive item on the agenda, such as the mentoring of nursing students, for example. Sarbjit gained an understanding of how formal meetings work and has been able to see how the team works collaboratively, under the leadership of Sarah the ward manager, to not only arrive at a solution but to use the ward information booklet to reinforce best practice in bedside handovers, which is something that Sarbjit will be able to take to her next ward-based placement.

To summarise our discussion on practice and practise, we could talk about Sarbjit learning to reflect on her practice in order to improve her practise and being aware that some aspects of her nursing care are governed by habit and custom that sit aside from government guidelines or hospital policy.

Although Sarbjit and Dave are engaging in practice-based and work-based learning for different reasons, the vignettes have demonstrated that both learners have a measure of curiosity that has assisted them in their workplace learning. We will now consider curiosity as a means of identifying opportunities for workplace learning.

Curiosity

Claridge and Lewis (2005) argue that curiosity starts with questions such as 'I wonder what...?', 'I wonder if...?' and 'I wonder how...?' and involves wondering, exploring and asking open questions that invite deeper thought. In Chapter 2 we explored change and learnt that health and social care settings are characterised by constant uncertainty. The development of curiosity is a useful learning strategy because it not only tolerates but embraces uncertainty, which is regarded as a pathway to understanding.

Sometimes you will be presented with different points of view that conflict with your current beliefs and therefore it is important for you to access information to resolve the uncertainties that trigger curiosity. In the vignettes we have seen the important role of the workplace mentor, who not only needs to be as curious as the learner but must collaborate with him or her to search for and identify appropriate learning solutions. This is particularly important when you need to develop sound knowledge to become competent with regards to a particular skill. Williams (2010) identified that learners need to demonstrate a 'learning-to-learn' aptitude to help them question assumptions about practice or what constitutes 'best practice' in a given situation, and this can only occur if learners have sufficient curiosity to seek information for themselves to resolve uncertainty or confusion through the generation of knowledge. The role of a workplace mentor is critical to the development of a learning-to-learn aptitude, for which curiosity is essential. In the next section we will identify some skills that will enable you to manage your relationship with your workplace mentor.

Managing your mentor

All of the vignettes have illustrated the work of workplace mentors. But why do we need mentors, what are their characteristics, and how can we best manage our mentor relationships? In relation to Sarbjit on her first placement, you will recall how important her workplace mentor Mandy was in assisting her to adapt to a new clinical area. Ousey (2009) argues that not only are mentors essential in preparing learners for their professional role, but they should facilitate the socialisation of students. Socialisation of students enables them to feel that they 'fit in' and are welcome and made to feel a valued member of the team rather than a 'newcomer'. As outlined by Gopee (2011, p. 21), there are many other reasons why mentors are necessary. Mentors should provide:

- Guidance and support
- A structured working environment for learning
- Constructive and honest feedback
- De-briefing following good or bad placement experiences
- Questioning and encouragement
- Protection from poor practice
- A link between theory and practice.

This requires workplace mentors to be role models who are capable of assessing your competency in a friendly manner using skills related to counselling, learning, teaching and instruction. Mentoring therefore requires someone to be patient, open-minded, approachable and knowledgeable, and to utilise good listening and communication skills in a tactful, diplomatic and confident manner. Being a workplace mentor is a big responsibility! Research suggests that in general, workplace mentors benefit from fulfilling their role as it improves their capacity for learning, although it is evident that not all mentors feel as prepared or supported as they would have liked, and the role does require a considerable amount of their time (Billett, 2003; Webb and Shakespeare, 2008; Fitzgerald et al, 2010; Bennett and McGowan, 2014).

Activity 18

Put yourself in the shoes of your mentor:

1. Identify at *least six qualities* that you think a practice-based or work-based learner should possess
2. Provide a *rationale* for each quality by explaining why it is pivotal to the relationship between a learner and his or her mentor.

The Royal College of Nursing (2006, pp. 2–3) has highlighted the following key responsibilities for students engaging in practice-based learning:

Preparing to start a placement:

- Read the course programme and student handbooks in order to make sense of the obligations of your university and each practice placement provider
- Obtain a copy of the placement profile that describes the placement or speak to a university link lecturer or placement officer to make sense of what will be expected of you while on placement
- Contact the placement and be sure you know what time shifts start and finish and whether clinical uniform is required, and if not what the uniform policy of the university and placement provider requires.

During a placement:

- Be proactive in seeking out learning experiences that are appropriate for your level of practice and competence with the support of your mentor
- Demonstrate a willingness to work as part of the team and participate in the delivery of safe patient care
- Learn to express your needs and adopt a questioning, reflective approach to your learning within the multidisciplinary team
- Use your mentor for guidance and support to enable you to achieve your learning outcomes and satisfactorily complete your practice assessments
- Seek help from appropriate clinical managers and/or link lecturers in a timely manner if the mentor relationship is not working to enable the achievement of the learning outcomes
- Ensure that the clinical skills required at each stage in your programme are attempted under the supervision of a skilled practitioner, with comments (feedback) provided by both you and your mentor
- Utilise learning opportunities outside the practice placement and, where possible, work with specialist practitioners
- Identify the role of professionals within other contexts of the organisation or community, e.g. radiographers, pharmacists, outpatient service providers
- Give and receive constructive feedback, e.g. on your placement feedback
- Reflect on your progress to increase your self-awareness, confidence and competence.

Raising and escalating a concern

Raising or escalating a concern is sometimes referred to as 'whistle-blowing'. If you witness an incident relating to a patient, carer, relative, service user or a member of staff who you are concerned or worried about, it is critical that you raise your concerns at the earliest opportunity. Each placement provider will have its own policy on raising or escalating a concern. Your university will also have a policy advising you on how to raise a concern while on placement.

Activity 19

If you are a work-based learner, access and read your employer's policy and your university department's student policy on raising or escalating concerns. If you are a practice-based learner, access and read your placement provider and university department's student policies on raising or escalating concerns.

Make notes on:

■ Examples of areas, situations or incidents of possible concern
■ Safeguarding of children and adults
■ How to report a concern
■ Who to report a concern to
■ Sources of support if you feel you need to report a concern.

Preparing for your practice-based assessment

In the last section of this chapter we will explore how you can prepare for your first practice-based assessment. Managing your relationship with your mentor is particularly important when preparing for a practice-based assessment. It is vital that you read and make sense of the practice assessment documentation that you and your mentor will be using as there may be sections that you will be asked to complete. For example, you may be asked to identify your learning outcomes (what you want to be able to achieve by the end of your placement) and how you intend to meet them, including resources, learning experiences and strategies to help you achieve each learning outcome. You may also be expected to reflect on your progress and provide some written comments on your performance, at the mid-point of your placement for example. But first we will explore why practice-based assessments are necessary and what we mean by competence.

Competence

It is likely that you will have been examined and assessed many times before, either at school, college or in the workplace, particularly if you have undertaken NVQ awards. It is, however, worth reminding yourself of why assessments are necessary. Gopee (2011, pp. 174–7) describes assessments as a period of purposeful observation and questioning that is undertaken to ascertain your ability to perform particular clinical interventions in accordance with established guidelines. Assessments also require you to demonstrate knowledge and provide a rationale for your actions. Assessors assess you in order to:

- Establish and authorise you as a developing healthcare professional to practise specific clinical skills without supervision
- Inform you of the level of your achievement at a point in time
- Judge your cognitive (knowledge and thinking), psychomotor (dexterity in clinical skills) and affective (professional/personal attitudes) skills
- Enable you to identify further learning needs
- Ascertain your overall competence and fitness to practice.

Competencies tend to focus on the skills and characteristics required by you to fulfil a particular job role through the use of written performance standards that are specific to a professional group and that can be assessed to identify or determine a particular level of practice (Garavan and McGuire, 2001).

Table 6.2 gives an example of three competencies that have been used to assess trainee assistant practitioners like Dave. You will see that all three competencies relate to communication skills and require the learner to be assessed in four different ways, with regards to safe practice, effective and efficient practice and the ability to demonstrate sound knowledge. This demonstrates that an area such as communication would need to be assessed not only by observing the performance of a learner's communication skills, but what he or she knows and understands regarding communication. In order for a learner to 'demonstrate sound knowledge', he or she would need to demonstrate his

Table 6.2 Competencies used to assess trainee assistant practitioners

Competency	Carries out the competency safely	Carries out the competency effectively	Carries out the competency efficiently	Demonstrates sound knowledge	Unsafe practice
Communicate with a range of clients relating to a range of matters in a form that is appropriate and is consistent with legislation, policies and procedures					
Improve the effectiveness of communication through the use of communication skills while managing barriers to communication					
Keep accurate and complete records consistent with legislation, policies and procedures					

or her knowledge of how he or she might communicate with clients using different techniques, explanations or instructional approaches. He or she would also need to identify and explain which workplace policies and legislation are relevant to verbal and non-verbal communication. The assessor would be required to assess the student and insert his or her signature and date against each competency. Additionally, the assessor would be required to provide written feedback to the student and insert his or her full name and job title onto the document to confirm that the assessment had been completed satisfactorily.

Competence is an important aspect of learning in workplaces because learning, as discussed earlier, is largely informal where knowledge is hidden and, as we saw in Vignette 11, is based on actions that are instinctive and intuitive. In other words, much of the learning within the workplace is through 'doing', using a range of activities which involves your emotions and forms your identity as you adapt to the world in which you live and work (Gonczi, 2004).

Practice-based assessments: what to expect

It is beyond the scope of this book to explain every type of practice-based assessment that could or should be undertaken in a health and social care setting. There are, however, two types of assessments that are commonly used. A formative assessment is a practice assessment that is used to develop and prepare you for your final assessment. Formative assessments are not usually allocated a pass or fail because they are developmental and provide you with an opportunity to 'do a dry run' and identify your areas of weakness. Workplace mentors should give you written as well as verbal feedback during and after a formative assessment to help you identify your areas for development and formulate an action plan. Quite often learners will have several formative assessments to prepare them for their final assessment, which is termed summative. A summative assessment is where an assessor observes you in practice. Summative assessments are usually pass or fail and require you to be observed in practice within a set assessment period. *Table 6.2* shows that in addition to a learner having his or her safety, effectiveness, efficiency and soundness of knowledge assessed, there is a column for 'unsafe practice', which if observed would lead to an automatic fail. At the end of a summative assessment, the assessor should provide you with written feedback. Not only is this important if you have failed, but it is important to enable you to realise that there are still areas for improvement and further development if you pass a summative assessment.

Being assessed in practice can be a stressful experience, and workplace mentors and assessors will know this from their own experiences of being assessed. As we saw with Dave in Vignette 10, formative assessments are not only valuable learning opportunities but they enable learners to minimise levels of stress and anxiety associated with final summative assessments. Price (2012) argues that learners require consistent mentoring within the practice context in which the assessment and the performance is to be assessed to ensure that there are 'no surprises' for learners, assessors and mentors. Workplace mentors and assessors therefore need to consult with each other to ensure that you will be assessed fairly and objectively, and that what is regarded as appropriate professional behaviour is understood by all.

Summary

In this chapter we have identified how learning takes place at work and have seen that most workplace learning is informal and coincides with work activities. Vignette 10 showed how Dave learnt about assessment skills when working with Kate and Vignette 11 featuring Sarbjit demonstrated the importance of how learning occurs through collaborative working. We also identified how non-theoretical knowledge is generated within particular clinical settings and how it helps practitioners to practice knowingly.

Developing your relationship with your mentor is critical as the workplace mentor role is demanding and requires a wide range of skills. How you manage your mentor is particularly important when preparing for practice-based assessments. These assessments focus on your competence and should provide you with verbal and written feedback to enable you to develop your practise to a safe, efficient and effective standard while demonstrating sound knowledge that will enable you to provide a rationale for your actions.

In the next chapter we will focus on the precise nature of your role and practice, and the characteristics of your clients and service users.

Key points

- In work-based and practice-based learning, working and learning occur simultaneously
- The tasks we complete while working are influenced by the nature of the work, while work is influenced by the nature of the learning that occurs; the two are complementary
- Workers have to balance the needs of being a worker and a learner, as working requires a service to be provided while learning is concerned with acquiring knowledge
- Informal learning at work arises when we perform a task, from how we perform within our role, our levels of awareness and understanding, our knowledge and skills, our personal development, our ability to make decisions and solve problems, our ability to work within a team and how we use our judgement
- Practice describes the carrying out, or the exercise, of a profession
- Practise means doing or exercising the skills of one's trade or profession; or to 'exercise one's professional skill'
- Curiosity is a learning-to-learn strategy that involves wondering, exploring and asking open questions that invite deeper thought to enable new knowledge to be generated and to alleviate uncertainty
- Learners need to manage their mentor relationships to ensure that practice-based assessments are successful
- Mentors and mentees must familiarise themselves with practice-based assessment documentation in preparation for such assessments to ensure that there are no surprises
- Practice-based assessments usually comprise formative or developmental assessments that are undertaken to prepare the student for final summative assessments.

Useful websites

- NHS Employers staff guidance on raising a concern: www.nhsemployers. org/your-workforce/retain-and-improve/raising-concerns-at-work-and-whistleblowing

- PAN-London Practice Assessment Document (example): www.herts. ac.uk/__data/assets/pdf_file/0004/43582/PLPAD-FINAL-Adult-Part-1-Sample.pdf
- Raising a concern to the Care Quality Commission (CQC): www.cqc.org. uk/file/5073
- Royal College of Nursing: Helping Students get the Best from Their Practice Placements: www.ed.ac.uk/polopoly_fs/1.50823!/fileManager/ RCNHelpingStudentsgetthebestfromtheirPracticePlacements.pdf

References

Bennett M, McGowan B (2014) Assessment matters – mentors need support in their role. *Br J Nurs* **23**(9): 454–8

Berg SA, Chyung SYY (2008) Factors that influence informal learning in the workplace. *Journal of Workplace Learning* **20**(4): 229–44

Billett S (2001) Learning through work: workplace affordances and individual engagement. *Journal of Workplace Learning* **13**(5): 209–14

Billett S (2003) Workplace mentors: demands and benefits. *Journal of Workplace Learning* **15**(3): 105–13

Billett S (2008) Learning through work: exploring instances of relational interdependencies. *International Journal of Educational Research* **47**(4): 232–40

Boud D, Solomon N (2001) *Work-based Learning: a New Higher Education.* Open University Press, Buckingham

Claridge MT, Lewis M (2005) *Coaching for Effective Learning: a Practical Guide for Teachers in Health and Social Care.* Radcliffe Publishing, Oxford

Engeström Y (2005) *Developmental Work Research – expanding activity theory in practice.* Lehmanns Media, Berlin

Eraut M (2004) Informal learning in the workplace. *Studies in Continuing Education* **26**(2): 247–73

Fitzgerald M, Gibson F, Gunn K (2010) Contemporary issues relating to assessment of pre-registration nursing students in practice. *Nurse Educ Pract* **10**(3): 158–63

Garavan TN, McGuire D (2001) Competencies and workplace learning. *Journal of Workplace Learning* **13**(4): 144–63

Gonczi A (2004) The new professional and vocational education. In: Foley G, ed. *Dimensions of Adult Learning: Adult Education and Training in a Global Era*. Open University Press, Buckingham: 19–34

Gopee N (2011) *Mentoring and Supervision in Healthcare*. 2nd edn. Sage, London

Jarvis P (2009) *Learning to be a Person in Society*. Routledge, London

Ousey K (2009) Socialization of student nurses – the role of the mentor. *Learning in Health and Social Care* **8**(3): 175–84

Price B (2012) Key principles in assessing students' practice-based learning. *Nurs Stand* **26**(49): 49–55

Royal College of Nursing (2006) *Helping Students get the Best from Their Practice Placements: a Royal College of Nursing Toolkit*. Royal College of Nursing, London

Webb C, Shakespeare P (2008) Judgements about mentoring relationships in nurse education. *Nurse Educ Today* **28**(5): 563–71

Wenger E (1998) *Communities of Practice: Learning, Meaning and Identity*. Cambridge University Press, Cambridge

Williams C (2010) Understanding the essential elements of work-based learning and its relevance to everyday clinical practice. *J Nurs Manag* **18**(6): 624–32

CHAPTER 7

Becoming a health and social care professional

By the end of this chapter you will be able to:

1. Identify a range of effective job-seeking activities
2. Evaluate professionalism and ethical principles
3. Analyse the concept of authentic professional practice
4. Explain how to support the learning of others.

Introduction

In this chapter we will explore the nature of becoming a health and social care professional by identifying the practical skills and fundamental requirements needed to secure employment, before exploring the nature of what it means to practice in a manner that is ethically sound. The concept of authenticity will be explored with regard to being a professional, and the chapter will conclude with a consideration of coach–mentoring as a means of creating and sustaining a learning culture within clinical and therapeutic areas.

Securing your first post

Nearly all posts in health, social care and nursing are advertised on the internet and require you to complete an online application form. In some respects this can be easier, in the sense that you can copy and paste personal information such as your educational qualifications, experience and employment history

Activity 20

Go onto the internet, find and browse the NHS jobs website:

1. Identify at least six features of the application process.
2. Explore the website and identify at least three resources to assist you in job seeking.
3. Using the search facilities, identify at least four local employers.
4. Using the search facilities, search for a post using an appropriate job title such as 'healthcare assistant', 'assistant practitioner', 'health trainer' or 'staff nurse'. Alternatively, search using a keyword such as 'urology', 'pain', 'smoking cessation', 'community health' or 'public health'.
5. Now try and limit your search using the filters, based on distance, pay scale, staff group or salary.
6. Once you have identified a job that is of interest, click on the job title, read the advertisement and download the job description and person specification document (these are usually a PDF documents).
7. Read the job description and person specification carefully and use the yellow text highlighter, which can be found in the task bar at the top of the document, to highlight keywords and information.
8. Finally, study the person specification and the essential and desirable requirements of the post-holder. This will include what education and qualifications are required, the knowledge and experience the post-holder must have, and their skills, abilities or attributes.

You may wish to repeat this activity using Universal Jobmatch at www.gov.uk/jobsearch. Alternatively, you may wish to search for jobs by identifying private health and social care providers in your locality and visiting the job vacancy section on their websites.

directly into the application form from an electronic document such as your curriculum vitae or resumé. You will need to create a new supporting statement for each post you apply for, however, in order to convince potential employers that you have a good understanding of both the post and the organisation.

You may find that websites provide specific services to support applicants, such as job alerts that require you to register on a prospective employer's website in order to receive notifications of new job vacancies via email.

Once you have identified a post that you wish to apply for:

- Make a note of the job title, department and the full name of the organisation.
- Make a note of the closing date for applications and the interview date, and use this information to plan your research, the completion of the application form, the writing of your supporting statement and the final submission of your application form.
- Read the job description and person specification carefully to ensure that you are eligible to apply for the post. You will need to meet all of the essential criteria but can still apply for a post if you do not fulfil all of the desirable criteria. Highlight keywords and key information.
- Make notes on the nature of the role (what type of person is required), the responsibilities (what you will be expected to do), the boundaries of the role (what you are not permitted to do and the scope of your practice) and the key skills and experience that is required.
- Most importantly, make sure that you have a thorough understanding of the needs of all the service users, clients and patients that you will be serving.
- Try and determine the membership of the multiprofessional team and what types of agencies and other organisations you may need to work in partnership with.
- Try to understand what personal attributes are required for the post. You may wish to return to the section on values in Chapter 6 to help you make sense of the kind of professional behaviour that your prospective employer is looking for.
- Search the company's or organisation's website to make sense of the services that it provides. Look for news stories relating to recent events and successes in order to understand what the organisation is best at and how it is performing. Try and find a copy of the company's or organisation's latest strategic plan and mission statement to make sense of its values, current strategic goals and key result areas.

The above checklist of activities will enable you to get a clear picture of the role that you are applying for and provide you with key information that will enable you to write your supporting statement.

Writing a supporting statement

If you are applying for a post online you will need to identify the word limit for your supporting statement. It is useful to prepare a draft in a separate electronic document before copying and pasting it into the electronic application form, as this will give you time to read, review, correct and edit the content. One approach to writing a supporting statement is to identify the key result areas for the post that you wish to apply for and to outline, by providing examples from your experience and making reference to your personal skills and attributes, how you would meet the key requirements. Here is another checklist that you can use to prepare and submit a supporting statement:

- Start by clearly identifying the post that you wish to apply for and make reference to the ward, department, service and organisation or employer.
- Create one sentence that summarises why you think this post is an 'unmissable opportunity'. Then describe your experience, skills and personal attributes and explain why they are relevant to each of the key result areas and essential criteria for the post.
- Use spare wordage to outline your recent successes, achievements and additional responsibilities that you have fulfilled during your current post, e.g. first aider, dignity champion, link healthcare assistant for infection control.
- Describe any recent study days or conferences that you have attended, and explain what impact they have had on your role, practice and patient care.
- Describe any courses that you are undertaking or have recently completed. Emphasise what particular challenges you have faced in completing the course, how you met those challenges and what the added value has been of your newly-acquired skills, knowledge and understanding to the development of your character, role, practice and patient care.
- Finally, summarise what kind of professional you wish to be if you are offered the post, how your role would be pivotal and what value you could add to the team, department and the wider organisation.

Vignette 12 demonstrates the job application process.

Vignette 12: Sarbjit applies for her first staff nurse post

Sarbjit had received a letter from the university confirming the award of her BSc (Hons) degree in adult nursing. While awaiting the arrival of her registration number from the Nursing and Midwifery Council, she started to search for her first staff nurse post. Having accessed the NHS jobs website, Sarbjit came across a post on the urology ward where she had undertaken her first placement. Although Sarbjit had enjoyed her placement, she realised that 3 years had elapsed since then and so she decided to visit the hospital website to find out what services were currently provided by the urology department. She discovered a news story about a successful fundraising campaign to purchase two portable bladder scanners and discovered that a new consultant urological surgeon and nurse practitioner had been appointed to develop services for men with prostate cancer.

Sarbjit downloaded the job description and person specification and decided to create a mind map to enable her to make sense of the essential and desirable criteria for the staff nurse post and to explore her knowledge, skills, capabilities and nursing experience to date. Creating a mind map was useful for Sarbjit because she was able to explore her own interests, passions and ambitions. Sarbjit remembered her first mentor, Mandy, and how she had supported and nurtured her throughout her placement. Sarbjit considered how she could become involved in mentoring as a staff nurse. She recalled how enthusiastic Mandy had been in supporting learners. Although Sarbjit realised that it would be a while before she could undertake the mentorship course, she reflected on her experiences of being approached by junior nursing students and HCAs for help with their learning while she had been on her final placement. She also discovered that the urology ward had started to develop assistant practitioner roles that required coach–mentoring by qualified staff in order to engage in work-based learning.

Armed with this information, Sarbjit set about writing her supporting statement by emphasising her experience working in a nursing home before university and the different skills, knowledge and understanding gained from each of her placements. Sarbjit described one of her personal attributes as 'approachability', and cited examples of when first- and second-year nursing students had sought help and advice from her. Sarbjit ended her supporting statement by expressing her interest in supporting the learning and development of trainee assistant practitioners, which she felt would prepare her for undertaking the mentorship course.

Although Sarbjit is interested in applying for a post on the ward where she has previously worked, she has completed some research into what changes have taken place in the department by accessing the hospital website and updating her knowledge of the ward and department. This is important because Sarbjit cannot rely on her previous understanding of the department or assume that staff will remember her from the placement. More importantly, Sarbjit must create a supporting statement that captures all of her experiences and how her knowledge and understanding have developed since the completion of her degree. Sarbjit's supporting statement must also be 'forward facing' in the sense of not only identifying what skills she can bring to the post, but what skills she would realistically like to develop following her appointment based on the opportunities that the ward may afford her.

Preparing for professional practice

What does it actually mean to be a professional? What is professional practice? Jasper (2006) states that at a fundamental level, professional practice is about what we do as a result of being registered with a professional body. Professional bodies such as the Health and Care Professions Council and the Nursing and Midwifery Council lay down codes of professional conduct and other statements of proficiency. However, being a professional is also shaped by:

- The legal system, e.g. nursing, medicine and radiography are regulated by law
- Government policy
- Service users who have expectations of how healthcare professionals act and carry out their duties
- The general public and the media, who construct certain images of healthcare professionals
- Professional opinion formers and leaders
- Other professions who have their own views on the role and function of specific healthcare professional groups.

(Jasper, 2006, pp. 217–18)

Additionally, professional behaviour for support workers in adult health and social care settings is shaped by standards set by Skills for Health, the sector's skills council, which has produced documents outlining minimum standards of training and a code of conduct for support workers including healthcare assistants and assistant practitioners.

Activity 21

Think about an experience of when you came into contact with a healthcare professional as a service user or patient:

1. What sort of professional behaviour did you expect to encounter during a consultation?
2. What impact do you think the media has on the perceptions of the general public in relation to professional practice?
3. What effect do you think that the media has on the professional practice of healthcare professionals?

Jasper (2006, p. 218) states that professional practice is characterised by the requirement of *higher education* (increasingly through a degree course), having a *body of knowledge* and theory, providing a *vital human service*, possessing *autonomy* and *accountability*, involving work that is *altruistic* (e.g. caregiving, or giving of oneself) and having a *code of ethics*. Embodying some, let alone all, of the virtues into your day-to-day practice seems daunting; however, Beauchamp and Childress (2001) have developed four very well-known and frequently-cited ethical principles:

- *Autonomy:* This is a word that we have already come across. It means respecting someone's own choices and relates to a patient, client or service user making his or her own decisions. It can also be described as self-government.
- *Non-maleficence:* In a nutshell, this means to 'do no harm'.
- *Beneficence:* This is the complete opposite of maleficence, and means 'to do good'.
- *Justice:* This means fairness, but in relation to health and social care it can relate to someone's ability to access services or how resources are managed.

Activity 22 will enable you to make sense of these ethical principles as they relate to an incident from clinical practice.

Activity 22

Mr Smith complains of a headache. Nurse B (who is a nurse prescriber) administers 1g of paracetamol to Mr Smith. Mr Smith becomes unwell, as he is allergic to paracetamol. Nurse B had forgotten to check whether Mr Smith had any drug allergies.

Let us consider which ethical principles are relevant in this scenario. One would be beneficence, as Nurse B was acting in such a way as to 'do good' by seeking through her practice to alleviate Mr Smith's pain. In failing to check for any allergies, however, Nurse B failed to 'do no harm'; in other words she failed to be non-maleficent.

Now think of a similar scenario or incident that illustrates autonomy and justice in relation to your own practice, but identify both 'best practice' and what would constitute poor practice.

There are a number of different ethical approaches that are used in medicine, health and social care. Together, the four ethical principles that Beauchamp and Childress (2001) describe what is known as a consequentialist approach. This is concerned with what the consequences might be of a particular action. As we saw in the case of Mr Smith and Nurse B, however, there is a big difference between what the consequences might be as opposed to the actual outcome. Almost everything we do in health and social care has some ethical consideration. Ethics is therefore not just about the 'big' issues, such as termination of pregnancy, organ transplantation, end-of-life issues or euthanasia.

Professional authenticity

You will recall in Chapter 3 that the final stage of the Me, My, More, Must model of reflection required you to identify the values that shape the healthcare professional that you aspire to be. In this chapter we have considered ethical principles and identified the elements of professional practice. In the next section we will explore the concept of professional authenticity, which we will use to bring together values, ethics and professionalism.

Activity 23

Visit either the Nursing and Midwifery Council or the Skills for Health website and download either The Code: Professional Standards of Practice and Behaviour for Nurses and Midwives (Nursing and Midwifery Council, 2015) or the Code of Conduct for Healthcare Support Workers and Adult Social Care Workers in England (Skills for Health, 2013):

1. Select at least six standards from your chosen code of conduct
2. Identify a practical example of how each standard could be breached and which ethical principle would be relevant to your chosen standards.

Throughout this book the vignettes featuring Sarbjit and Dave have demonstrated that learning in practice is concerned with developing ways of being and becoming a healthcare professional, rather than simply acquiring skills and knowledge. Often practice-based learners are placed in situations that are similar and require them to give care that they have given before. Practice-based learners need to develop the ability to see the familiar or everyday in a new light in order to develop their practise. Dall'Alba (2009, pp. 43–4) argues that reshaping our assumptions about what it means to be a particular professional, such as a teacher or therapist, leads to new ways of being that involve a transformation of ourselves. In essence, our engagement in practise, even in situations that are familiar to us, shape how we become the healthcare professional that we wish to become, but only when we are prepared to see the everyday differently and recognise when experiences arising from the delivery of care are significant to the creation of our professionalism. This type of professional learning is called 'authentic' (Webster-Wright, 2010, p. 113). Authentic professional learning has the following constituents:

- Understanding, which leads to a change from what you previously knew (your prior understanding) through a transition that has changed your understanding as a professional. This requires you to know what to do, how to think and to question what is done. For example, in Chapter 1 we saw how Sarbjit had some previous experience of death and dying but she found the experience of the sudden death of a patient following cardiac arrest and how patients looked to her for reassurance (as a nurse) during the arrest a deeply challenging experience.

- Engagement requires you to be actively engaged in care and to care about specific aspects of practice while recognising that some aspects of care are uncertain. In Chapter 2, we saw how Sarbjit re-engaged with the cardiac arrest situation through reflection to make sense of some of the uncertainties that she had experienced regarding her role and her responsibilities during the incident.
- Interconnection: Authentic professional learning arises from multiple experiences. In order to connect those experiences over time, you need to harness your imagination to draw together your past, present and future and to engage with others (such as workplace mentors) in a dynamic way that uses shared experiences to create understanding. In Chapter 4 we saw how Dave sought to develop his skills of assessment, not only by being supervised undertaking a Berg balance assessment of Mr Shah, but by asking whether he could undertake further assessments and learning from observing Kate assess patients.
- Openness: Authentic professional learning requires you to be 'open-ended' by developing an attitude that recognises the opportunities and constraints that exist within professional environments and how tensions that arise in practice settings can be resolved. In Chapter 5 we saw how Dave engaged in a 'conversation that mattered' in order to make sense of his identity as a trainee assistant practitioner in the context of a team that was preparing to support the learning of two newly-qualified healthcare professionals.

Authentic professional learning is essential to the creation and ongoing development of authentic professional practice. Webster-Wright (2010, pp. 171–88) argues that the way a professional continues to learn is an expression of his or her way of being a professional in a dynamic interplay with his or her particular professional context. Professional authenticity arises from learning that is transformative. This is achieved when you seek to face up to situations by weighing up different possibilities and seeking to understand your professional responsibilities. This requires you to engage in constant cycles of reorientation that are shaped by changing circumstances while maintaining a continuous sense of yourself as a professional person.

Supporting the learning of others

The Berwick Review (National Advisory Group on the Safety of Patients in England, 2013) into patient safety within the NHS following the failures in care highlighted by the Mid-Staffordshire inquiry (Francis Report, 2013) and the Keogh Review (2013) into the quality of care and treatment provided by 14 hospital trusts in England, recommended that the NHS should seek to become 'a learning organisation'. The Berwick Review concluded that an ethic of learning was essential to the reduction of patient harm through the embracing of a culture of learning and improvement. Throughout this book we have examined practical examples of the value of mentors and mentorship. In this section we explore the concepts of mentoring and coaching. This book has been written at a time when the nature of educational provision for healthcare assistants, nursing students and qualified nurses faces further changes as the Nursing and Midwifery Council seeks to respond to the recommendations of the Willis Review (2015).

The words 'coach' and 'mentor' suggest the very nature of the activity of both roles, in the sense of 'boarding' a coach to undertake a journey and being encouraged to think through the support of someone else. A mentor is a person who helps another to think things through. Mentorship comprises of the following activities:

'Managing a relationship with a learner
Encouragement of the learner, by providing support and feedback
Nurturing, to enable a learner to progress and develop
Teaching, through explanation, demonstration and instruction
Offering, by providing a learner with a menu of learning opportunities
Responding to a learner's needs to ensure that the learner can build his or her confidence and become as self-directed as possible.'

(Mumford and Roodhouse, 2010, p. 62)

A coach is a person who helps someone to think through how to get from where he or she is to where he or she wants to be (Pask and Joy, 2004). The focus of coaching can vary, depending on the relationship between you and your coach. Within health and social care and clinical practice settings, coaching will focus on the performance of you as a learner and a practitioner.

Coaching and mentoring both have a place within health and social care, as we have seen with Sarbjit and Dave. In essence, Sarbjit as a nursing student benefitted from a traditional mentorship approach as she was being prepared for practice ahead of professional registration. Dave was already employed within a clinical area and had a distinct role that he was being prepared for as a trainee assistant practitioner. Consequently, Dave received coaching from Kate not only to learn new skills but to refine his existing knowledge in order to perform to a higher level. Foster-Turner (2005) argues that coach–mentoring in health and social care provides you with opportunities to learn from existing and novel situations by drawing on, interpreting and integrating information to support the development of new behaviours. One of the key goals of coaching and mentoring is to provide both the mentor and mentee with an opportunity to reflect on practice together. This creates a unique relationship where there is as much for the coach to learn as the participant (Raelin, 2008). Engaging in coaching and mentoring should lead to you becoming responsible for your own learning, which is a critical characteristic of adult learning. This is important because a placement or workplace setting can only provide you with so many learning opportunities, resources or affordances. Raelin (2008) argues that learners need to consult with a variety of knowledge resources and understand that work tasks can be tackled in multiple ways and that no one individual embodies all the necessary expertise.

Moving beyond 'how do you feel' and 'what do you think' questions

A key skill for any coach or mentor to develop is the ability to ask questions. I know from my own experience of being a student and being mentored in clinical practice that being asked repeatedly what I felt or thought became tiresome. As you become a more senior practice- or work-based learner, you will find that other students will seek you out and start to ask you questions that will require you to engage in coach–mentoring. Assisting learners to engage in deep learning requires you to use helpful questioning that stimulates their thinking, rather than provide them with answers (Cunningham et al, 2004). Two basic strategies that can be used with a learner to enable him or her to think and reflect involve 'framing' and 'reframing' (Foster-Turner, 2005).

Framing questions are used in 'real time' as a coach, mentor and learner are faced with an immediate opportunity for learning. Framing questions include the following:

- What outcome might arise from this situation for the patient?
- How else could this be?
- How different could the care have been given?
- What do you want from this learning experience?
- What really matters to you in all of this?
- Can we retrace out steps?
- How would it be if...?

The above questions are designed to help you question a learner at the time when he or she is involved in a learning opportunity that has arisen during, or just after, an episode of care; although it must be stated that incidents of care should not be discussed between the mentor and mentee 'above' the patient, client or service user.

Reframing questions tend to be retrospective and are best used when a learner, mentor or coach take 'time out' to sit and mutually reflect on a care situation, at the end of a shift for example.

These include the following:

- Let's look at this from another angle/stand in somebody else's shoes...
- On the one hand I hear you saying this... but on the other hand I hear you are also saying something else...
- If you had three wishes for your client, what would they be?
- If this were a story, what is the next part to be told?
- And what happens next?
- You seem surprised and puzzled; tell me, what is the muddiest point?

Reframing questions provide you as a coach–mentor with an opportunity to ask longer questions that require the learner to reflect deeply. This provides you with an opportunity to 'regroup' and to anticipate your own response, not only to the question he or she has asked, but to the answer from the learner. You will see that the last question 'What is the muddiest point?' contains a metaphor that may have generated an image in your mind of a muddy (as opposed to clear) puddle. Metaphors are useful devices that can bring your questioning skills to life. For example, as a personal tutor with my own students, when I sense that a tutorial is drawing to a close I will often ask my tutee to tell me what the 'take home' or 'take away' messages are from the meeting. Both these phrases have a metaphorical value that suggest food and present the coach or mentor with an opportunity to ask open-ended questions of learners that are structured in an interesting and novel way.

Summary

In a sense, the act of becoming a health and social care professional starts from the very first and earliest practice experiences of the learner. This is because becoming and being a professional is inextricably linked to the learning that occurs through experience. Securing your first post will require you to revisit the process of becoming and to analyse its key features against the essential and desirable requirements of the post in order to convince a prospective employer that hiring you is as much an unmissable opportunity for them as for you. The professional values that you hold will inevitably shape the professional you become. The nature of your professional practice, however, is shaped by a range of expectations that arise from the public, the requirements of professional bodies that produce codes of conduct, the acquisition of a higher education award, the maintenance of a knowledge base, your skills and competency. Underpinning your professionalism is a need to practise in an ethical manner to ensure that you not only do good but do no harm, while acting fairly and justly and in a way that places the autonomy of your patients, clients and service users at the forefront of your practice. Becoming an authentic professional requires you to 'see the everyday differently' and recognise when experiences arising from the delivery of care are significant to the creation of your professionalism. In order to work in learning organisations you need to use the best principles of coaching and mentoring to ensure that others are learning not only with you but from you, and that you are actively seeking to grasp learning opportunities that enable a deep and mutually reflective approach to learning. In the final chapter we will identify and bring together the threads and central message of this book to determine how practice- and work-based learning can be a compelling force for change.

Key points

- Crafting a supporting statement for each post you apply for is essential if you are to convince a potential employer that you have a good understanding of both the post and the organisation that you are seeking employment with
- A supporting statement must be 'forward facing' in the sense of not only identifying what skills you can bring to the post, but what skills you would realistically like to develop following your appointment
- Professional practice is determined by: your professional regulating body; standards contained within codes of conduct; legislation; government policy; the expectations of the public and service users with regard to how we act and carry out our duties; pressure groups and opinion formers; and the influence of other health and social care professionals and sector skills councils
- Authentic professional learning occurs when we develop understanding that leads to change: when we become actively engaged in care while recognising that some aspects of care are uncertain; when we harness our imagination to draw together our past, present and future; when we engage with others in way that uses shared experiences to create understanding; when we develop an attitude that recognises the opportunities and constraints that exist within professional environments and resolve tensions that arise in practice settings
- Helping to develop and sustain a learning culture requires you to understand, adopt and adapt the best principles of coaching and mentoring that includes the ability to use questions that 'frame' and 'reframe' learning experiences for the benefit of learners and yourself.

Useful websites

- Health and Care Professionals Council: www.hpc-uk.org
- NHS Jobs: www.jobs.nhs.uk
- Nursing and Midwifery Council: www.nmc.org.uk
- Skills for Health: www.skillsforhealth.org.uk
- Universal Jobmatch: www.gov.uk/jobsearch

References

Beauchamp TL, Childress JF (2001) *Principles of Biomedical Ethics*. 5th edn. Oxford University Press, Oxford

Cunningham I, Dawes G, Bennett B (2004) *The Handbook of Work Based Learning*. Gower Publishing Limited, Aldershot

Dall'Alba G (2009) Learning professional ways of being: ambiguities of becoming. In: Dall'Alba G, ed. *Exploring Education Through Phenomenology: Diverse Approaches*. Wiley-Blackwell, Oxford: 41–52

Foster-Turner J (2005) *Coaching and Mentoring in Health and Social Care: the Essential Manual for Health Professionals and Organisations*. Radcliffe Publishing, Oxford

Francis Report (2013) Report of the Mid-Staffordshire NHS Foundation Trust Public Inquiry. www.midstaffspublicinquiry.com/report (accessed 17 November 2015)

Jasper M (2006) *Professional Development, Reflection and Decision-making*. Blackwell Publishing, Oxford

Keogh B (2013) Review into the Quality of Care and Treatment Provided by 14 Hospital Trusts in England: Overview Report. www.nhs.uk/NHSEngland/bruce-keogh-review/Documents/outcomes/keogh-review-final-report.pdf (accessed 17 November 2015)

Mumford J, Roodhouse S, eds (2010) *Understanding Work-based Learning*. Gower Publishing, Farnham

National Advisory Group on the Safety of Patients in England (2013) A Promise to Learn – a Commitment to Act: Improving the Safety of Patients in England. www.gov.uk/government/publications/berwick-review-into-patient-safety (accessed 17 November 2015)

Nursing and Midwifery Council (2015) The Code: Professional Standards of Practice and Behaviour for Nurses and Midwives. www.nmc.org.uk/globalassets/sitedocuments/nmc-publications/revised-new-nmc-code.pdf (accessed 17 November 2015)

Pask R, Joy B (2007) *Mentoring–coaching: a Guide for Education Professions*. McGraw Hill/Open University Press, Maidenhead

Raelin J (2008) *Work-based Learning: Bridging Knowledge and Action in the Workplace*. Jossey-Bass, San Francisco

Skills for Health (2013) Code of Conduct for Healthcare Support Workers and Adult Social Care Workers in England. www.skillsforhealth.org.uk/standards/item/217-code-of-conduct (accessed 17 November 2015)

Webster-Wright A (2010) *Authentic Professional Learning: Making a Difference Through Learning at Work*. Springer, London

Willis P (2015) Raising the Bar. Shape of Caring: a Review of the Future Education and Training of Registered Nurses and Care Assistants. http://hee.nhs.uk/wp-content/blogs.dir/321/files/2015/03/2348-Shape-of-caring-review-FINAL.pdf (accessed 17 November 2015)

CHAPTER 8

Practice-based and work-based learning: ten key themes

By the end of this chapter you will be able to:

1. Discuss the similarities and differences between practice-based and work-based learning
2. Describe a range of strategies to engage in learning that fosters a learning culture
3. Evaluate the key skills that are necessary to be a skilled influencer
4. Identify behaviours that are necessary to become a change practitioner.

Introduction

In this final chapter we will pull together the central themes discussed throughout the book to enable you to become a health and social care practitioner who can initiate change through skilled influence.

Ten key themes

We started our journey into practice-based and work-based learning with a consideration of the nature of learning, which traditionally has relied on teachers using a questioning approach to uncover the assumptions, beliefs, values and hidden knowledge of learners. In Chapter 7 we explored some of the strategies used by coaches and mentors to frame and reframe questions, but the most important outcome of learning is when a learner's behaviour changes as a result of an experience. The primary value of being questioned by a teacher is for you to demonstrate your understanding. This occurs when you can provide an explanation not only for your actions, but for the course of action that you have taken based on your knowledge. Knowledge is quite different from information that, although readily available via the internet, is not the same as the knowledge that is acquired from learning through experience which equips you to practise.

The themes are:

1. Practice-based and work-based learning have key similarities and differences
2. Working for an organisation shapes your professional identity
3. Working and learning must coincide
4. Curiosity is the key to informal and opportunistic learning
5. A successful practice-based assessment requires careful planning
6. Differentiate your role from your practise, patients and service users
7. Hold conversations that matter
8. Minimise the gaps between theory and practice
9. Embrace change, uncertainty and supercomplexity
10. Lifelong learning is the key to authentic professional practice.

Theme 1: Practice-based and work-based learning have key similarities and differences

One of the key features of this book has been to differentiate practice-based learning from work-based learning, and this has been attempted through the use of a series of vignettes featuring Dave, a trainee assistant practitioner, and Sarbjit, a nursing student. We saw with Sarbjit that practice-based learning is used to prepare her for practice through a range of placements ahead of registration with a professional body. Work-based learning, as we saw with Dave, is learning that uses work and the workplace; it required him to balance the demands of fulfilling the role that he had been employed for with learning while remaining in a particular workplace. Practice-based and work-based learners may be supported by workplace mentors, who will be required to provide a range of skills that include debriefing; the assessment of a learner's competency, skills and knowledge; and reflection in and on practice events. Practice-based learning within particular professions such as nursing is characterised as education by and for a distinct professional group. Work-based learning is education that is orientated to standards of work that are required by the organisation in a general sense and the standards that are set within the team where the work-based learner, such as Dave, is situated.

Theme 2: Working for an organisation shapes your professional identity

We explored what it means to be in work and to work for an organisation. We saw that money, the level and variety of activity, and the personal satisfaction gained from work are as important as the reward arising from the completion of work. All workers are required to have a range of knowledge, skills and personal attributes that shape their motivation and engagement in work. Your work within health and social care organisations is characterised by change that is constant, normal and prevents care from becoming stagnant. As a result of the constant presence and influence of change, organisations have to plan and manage change carefully. Effective change management is necessary to offset the negative influence that change may have on employees.

Theme 3: Working and learning must coincide

One of the greatest challenges for you when engaging in work-based and practice-based learning is to ensure that working and learning occur simultaneously. One of the greatest threats to learning within health and social care organisations occurs when caregiving and learning are seen as separate activities. Learning and caregiving should be activities that coincide, as the tasks you complete while caregiving are influenced by the nature of work, while work is influenced by the nature of learning. Learning and caregiving should therefore not only be coincident but complementary. In order to achieve this synergy between working and learning, you have to balance the needs of being a worker and a learner, as working requires you to provide a service while learning is concerned with acquiring knowledge.

Theme 4: Curiosity is the key to informal and opportunistic learning

Learning within clinical and therapeutic environments, whether through work-based or practice-based learning, is regarded as informal rather than the traditional setting of a classroom or lecture theatre. Informal learning arises when you perform a task and is concerned with how you perform within your role. Your levels of awareness and understanding, your knowledge and skills, your personal development, your ability to make decisions and solve problems, your ability to work within a team and how you use your judgement are key factors in your ability to engage in informal learning. An important strategy for all learning within practice and workplace environments is the measure of curiosity that you bring to each practice encounter. Curiosity is a learning-to-learn strategy that involves wondering, exploring and asking open questions that invite deeper thought to enable new knowledge to be generated. It can also help you alleviate the uncertainty that characterises professional practice environments.

Theme 5: A successful practice-based assessment requires careful planning

All practice-based and work-based learners should be assessed on their performance to ensure that they are competent, safe, effective and efficient, and can demonstrate sound underpinning knowledge. As a learner you need to manage your relationship with your mentor or assessor carefully to ensure that practice-based assessments are successful and that there are no surprises. This requires you to be actively engaged in preparing, planning and arranging a variety of different assessments, including formative or developmental assessments that are undertaken to prepare for final summative assessments.

Theme 6: Differentiate your role from your practise, patients and service users

Having explored the context in which work-based and practice-based learning occurs, we sought to differentiate between our role and practise. This was achieved by asking ourselves who we were and what we did in practice in addition to identifying the boundaries of our responsibilities. We saw that mind mapping was a useful creative thinking tool that can help you make sense of your role, practice and service users.

One of the dangers of viewing yourself on the basis of the activities and tasks that you complete is that it can stop you from learning. Through this book, and as demonstrated in the vignettes, you have learnt that reflection is critically important to learning as it requires you to learn by noticing yourself. Additionally, reflection can provide you with an opportunity to explore how to work in partnership and collaboration with your colleagues. This is vital to contemporary health and social care practice, as it has a direct effect on the quality of care that service users receive. Paradoxically, some of the most inexperienced of health and social care workers have the most direct contact with patients and service users. 'Face workers', such as trainees, practice-based and work-based learners, become the face of an organisation because they have the most direct and constant contact with service users and their families. Engaging in reflection on your interactions with service users is important as it helps you to identify the abstract, technical, practical and conjectural forms of knowledge and the social or 'affective' skills that are required to provide excellent care. Furthermore, the acquisition of new skills and knowledge coupled with experience enables you to move from being a novice, experienced beginner and proficient worker towards becoming an expert.

Theme 7: Hold conversations that matter

Practice-based and work-based learning requires you to develop a range of effective communication skills to engage in learning that is self-directed. You saw that it is important for learners and mentors to be able to differentiate between debate and dialogue in order to hold conversations that matter. Holding conversations that matter is vital if learning opportunities are to be secured.

Learners and mentors need to view discussion as a form of inquiry that enables assumptions to be uncovered and new understanding to be created. This is particularly important if working and learning is to become integrated to form a strategy for all health and social care professionals to manage the change, uncertainty and the supercomplexity that exists within workplaces.

On a personal level, there are several key learning processes that will enable you to balance being a worker and a learner and include remembering, imitating, adapting, experimenting and reinforcing. These learning processes occur within the constant stream of experiences that arise in practice. You can pursue the answers to questions and retain your level of curiosity if you reflect and notice yourself.

Theme 8: Minimise the gaps between theory and practice

Learning in clinical and therapeutic environments can deliver some perplexing and confusing experiences. We saw that the disjuncture between what you expect to experience, as a result of your knowledge, and what is actually experienced when you come to put your knowledge into action can create what is called a theory–practice gap. Having a mentor who can provide guided learning can minimise the impact of theory–practice gaps by creating interdependence between your knowledge and engagement in workplace learning activities.

Theme 9: Embrace change, uncertainty and supercomplexity

You may not necessarily learn from everything you experience. Health and social care professionals need to become reflective practitioners in order to deal with the large volume of information and evidence that underpins practice and the challenge of working within modern organisations that are characterised by constant change, uncertainty and supercomplexity. Organisations require you to develop particular capabilities, such as learning through reflection, rather than being reliant on previous experience and old ways of working. Recently, there have been a number of high-profile cases that have been described as moral catastrophes and have led to recommendations for the promotion of learning organisations. This requires you to think, reason and reflect on your practice and values, which are your personal beliefs and attitudes about a person, object, idea or action. We saw that people organise their set of values internally along a continuum from most important to least important, and that value systems are held together by beliefs. Beliefs are assumptions that the individual accepts as being true. They shape an individual's attitudes and determine his or her way of thinking, behaving and feeling. The identification of your values is critical, as caregiving is the giving of oneself that requires you to be altruistic, compassionate, empathic, discerning and trustworthy while demonstrating integrity and conscientiousness.

In addition to the importance of values in health and social care, we saw that professional practice is determined by codes of conduct produced by professional regulatory bodies that contain standards. Legislation, government policy, and the expectations of the public, service users, pressure groups, opinion formers, sector skills councils and other health and social care professionals all influence how you act and carry out your duties.

Theme 10: Lifelong learning is the key to authentic professional practice

We explored the concept of authentic professional learning, which occurs when we develop understanding that leads to change. This occurs when you become actively engaged in care while recognising that some aspects of care remain uncertain. This requires you to harness your imagination and draw together your past, present and future by engaging with others in ways that use shared experiences to create understanding. Authentic professional learning requires you to have an attitude to your professional practice that is open-ended and that to be comfortable with the opportunities and constraints that exist within professional environments so you can actively resolve tensions that arise within health and social care environments. Authentic professional learning is necessary to create authentic professionals. Developing and sustaining a learning culture requires you to understand, adopt and adapt the best principles of coaching and mentoring to advance authentic professional practice. This brings us rather neatly back to the starting point of this book and our consideration of the use of questioning for learning that can 'frame' and 'reframe' learning experiences for the benefit of learners and ourselves.

Moving forward: being a skilled influencer

Developing the ability to become a skilled influencer takes time, experience and learning through observing how influential, successful and effective professionals practice. Skilled influencing is the ability to be astute rather than being manipulative or using your influence in a negative manner. The art of skilled influencing is important in order to effect change that will make a difference to the quality and delivery of health and social care.

We have already noted that in the face of change and uncertainty we cannot rely on previous strategies. It is important to reflect on the impact that your values have on others. Becoming a skilled influencer not only requires you to understand how your approach, style and beliefs differ from others; it requires you to influence change despite the working culture that may exist within a clinical or therapeutic team, department or organisation. The most effective form of influence arises when you have the ability to engage in dialogue and it requires you to ensure that you can persuade colleagues with a viewpoint that is formed logically and is supported by evidence. Dialogue will create an opportunity for communication where all parties can contrast and compare a range of options by exploring the relative advantages and disadvantages of each proposal.

Becoming a skilled influencer is the first step in providing leadership in areas of care that need development and improvement. This requires leadership by example, where you take your followers with you. Once you have arrived at a position where you know you have gained influence, it becomes necessary to identify the best behaviours that will enable you to deliver change as a practitioner.

Moving forward: becoming a change practitioner

It is beyond the scope of this book to look at theories of change, change management and why people within organisations become resistant to change.

Activity 21

Identify a successful or effective practitioner, or someone within your organisation that you regard as an inspirational role model. Arrange to spend a day shadowing him or her and identify:

1. How he or she organises and prioritises his or her work
2. How he or she manages his or her time
3. How he or she communicates with members of the multidisciplinary team
4. His or her leadership or managerial style
5. What continuing professional development opportunities he or she engages in.

Senior support workers and newly-qualified health and social care professionals, however, have a unique opportunity to initiate change by bringing their experience, knowledge and newly-developed skills from other departments and organisations to their first appointment. Keep (2001) observes that change practitioners are often facilitating change while undergoing change themselves, as we saw with Sarbjit and Dave. Seeking to change long-standing practices when you are new to an organisation is deeply challenging as it places you at risk of being isolated at a time when you are seeking to establish working relationships. In one sense, work-based learners such as Dave have an advantage as they already possess an in-depth understanding of their employing organisation. Challenges do arise for work-based learners if the change that they wish to initiate clashes with the opinions of colleagues with whom they may have longstanding working relationships. Those that are new to the organisation, such as Sarbjit, may have less of a concern about their immediate colleagues, but may be disadvantaged by not possessing knowledge of the culture of their workplace or organisation.

Keep (2001, p. 92) identifies a range of gold standard behaviours for change practitioners that include:

- *Being resilient* by maintaining a clear focus on the area for change and retaining the ability to continue to prioritise your work so that the area of change does not dominate your attention
- *Developing a sense of personal pride* by seeking to be associated with high standards of care and aiming to identify best practice
- *Demonstrating charisma and passion* through the demonstration of energy that is contagious and that can transform the feelings and perceptions of others

- *Being an effective communicator* by conveying ideas persuasively, clearly and concisely using the right communication channels and engaging the right audience
- *Being resourceful* through the identification of different ways of dealing with problems
- *Being dependable* by demonstrating a willingness to do 'what is expected'.

In order to become a change practitioner and to initiate change through skilled influencing, it is critical that you can identify when it is appropriate to work autonomously and collaboratively and vice versa; to initiate change and embed new ways of working that ensure engagement and ownership throughout the team. Working collaboratively will not only ensure that change is crafted as a result of sharing knowledge, skills experience and expertise, but that the process of change arising from skilled influence becomes an opportunity for learning within the workplace.

You will become the professional that you want to become

Practice-based and work-based learning, although pursued for different reasons and within different contexts, share key similarities that are critical to the health, productivity and prosperity of all health and social care organisations. Your engagement in authentic professional learning and values-based reflection will enable you to become an authentic practitioner who is committed to organisational learning and the learning of others while delivering excellent care.

Reference

Keep J (2001) The change practitioner: perspectives on role, effectiveness, dilemmas and challenges. In: Hamlin B, Keep J, Ash K, eds. *Organizational Change and Development: a Reflective Guide for Managers, Trainers and Developers*. Pearson Education, Harlow

Appendices

Appendix 1: Blank dartboard

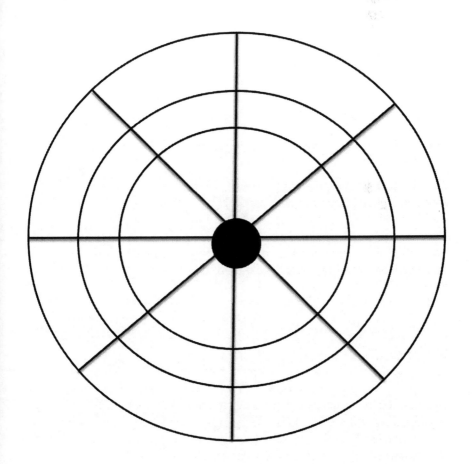

Appendix 2: SWOT analysis template

Strengths: **Weaknesses:**

Opportunities: **Threats:**

Appendix 3: PESTLE analysis template

Political	Economic	Social	Technological	Legal	Ethical
For example power-holders, governance, representation, key decision-makers, influence of policy, influences of government (local/national), disadvantaged groups or individuals, environmental concerns	For example funding, levels of public spending, budgets, private finance, contractual obligations, profit, loss, resource management and allocation, enterprise, competition, markets, globalisation, poverty	For example social and community relationships, community engagement, education, organisational culture, team culture, leadership, management, disadvantaged groups or individuals	For example impact of science, technology, research and development, use and availability of contracts, servicing, calibration and maintenance, functionality, information technology, software, support and training	For example law, legislation, law-making, case law, litigation, negligence, contractual obligations, human rights, vulnerable adults and children, safeguarding	For example medical ethics, business ethics, environmental resources, sustainability, social and moral responsibilities, values, shared decision-making, advocacy

Appendix 4: Blank learning agreement

Week commencing (dd/mm/yy)	Learning objective or learning activities	Resources	Module workbook	Assignment or project report	Tick and initial when completed

Signature of mentor:.. Date:................

Signature of student:... Date:................